Georgia
Its Heritage and Its Promise

Student Workbook

Frank Jones

CLAIRMONT PRESS
Atlanta, Georgia

The Author

Frank Jones, author of the Student Workbook, earned his M.A. in U.S. History at the University of Colorado at Denver and his M.Ed. from Georgia State University. He currently teaches middle school social studies in Gwinnett County. Prior to his teaching career, he served in the U.S. Army, and retired as a Lieutenant Colonel after 20 years of service around the world. Frank serves in various faculty leadership positions and has been a presenter at the National Council for the Social Studies annual conference. He is a member of the Georgia Council for the Social Studies and the National Council for the Social Studies.

Editor: Anna Welles

Design: Robin McDonald

Maps: Spatial Graphics; New Diameter Creative Services, Inc.

Georgia: Its Heritage and Its Promise — Workbook

Contents

Name_____   **Date**_____

Locate Georgia on a Map!

Directions: Use the boxes to sketch the location of Georgia.

The **nation** that Georgia belongs to:

The **region** of the country where Georgia is:

The **continent** that Georgia is a part of:

The **hemispheres** that Georgia belongs to:

Name_____ Date_____

Compare Georgia's Geographic Regions

Directions: After reading the information on pages 6-18, use the chart below to compare Georgia's five geographic regions.

	Soil Type (sandy, fertile, etc.)	Landforms (rolling hills, mountains, etc.)	Cities Found Here	Geographic Area of State (north, central, etc.)
Appalachian Plateau				
Valley and Ridge				
Blue Ridge Mountains				
Piedmont				
Coastal Plain				

Name_____ Date_____

Describe the Climate and Weather in Georgia

Directions: After reading the section on Georgia's climate and weather (pages 20-25), answer the following questions.

1. What is the difference between climate and weather? _____
    _____

2. What are the two most likely forms of extreme weather in Georgia? _____ and _____

3. What other types of extreme weather are likely to occur in Georgia? _____
    _____

4. How does the combination of Georgia's climate and soil conditions contribute to agricultural production? ____
    _____

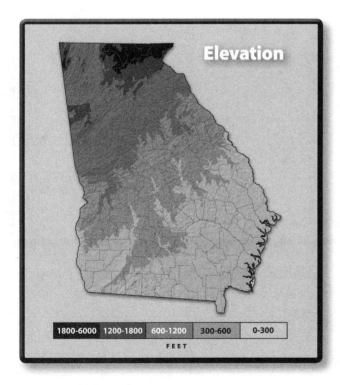

Elevation

| 1800-6000 | 1200-1800 | 600-1200 | 300-600 | 0-300 |

FEET

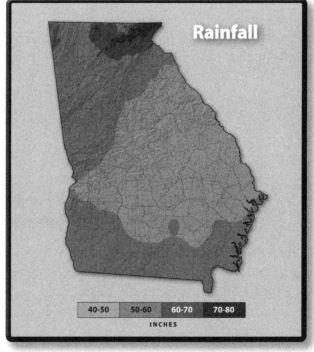

Rainfall

| 40-50 | 50-60 | 60-70 | 70-80 |

INCHES

5. Based on the maps above, how are rainfall amounts and elevation related in the state of Georgia? _____
    _____

6. How do climate and weather impact the people of Georgia? _____
    _____

Name_____ **Date**_____

Explore Georgia's Rivers

Directions: Use the map on the right to answer questions about Georgia's rivers.

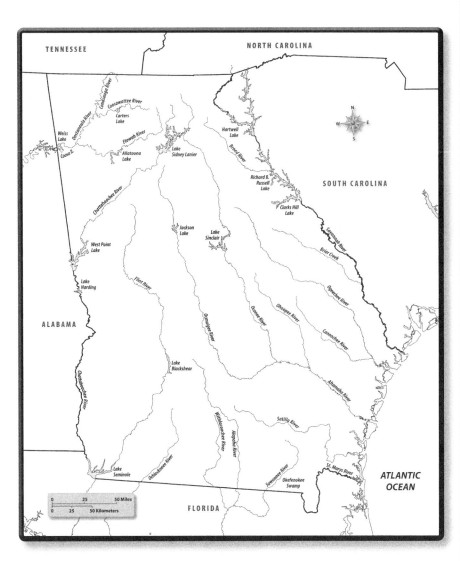

1. Which rivers form part of Georgia's border? Color them red.

   a._____

   b._____

   c._____

2. Which rivers flow into the Gulf of Mexico? Color them green.

   a._____

   b._____

   c._____

   d._____

3. Which rivers flow into the Atlantic Ocean? Color them blue.

   a._____

   b._____

   c._____

   d._____

   e._____

4. Which river is closest to your home? Color it purple.

   _____

Name_____   **Date**_____

Identify Key Geographic Features

Directions: Draw and label the specified regions, features, and rivers on the blank map of Georgia. Use colored pencils to make a key and to identify different items.

Key

Regions:

- ☐ Appalachian Plateau
- ☐ Valley and Ridge
- ☐ Blue Ridge Mountains
- ☐ Piedmont
- ☐ Coastal Plain

Features:

- ☐ Okefenokee Swamp
- ☐ Fall Line
- ☐ Appalachian Mountains
- ☐ Barrier islands

Rivers:

- ☐ Chattahoochee
- ☐ St. Marys
- ☐ Savannah

Name_____   **Date**_____

Practice Map Skills

Directions: Use the map on the opposite page to answer questions and accomplish the tasks below.

1. If your town/city is not on the map, draw it in and label it. If your town/city is on the map, circle it.

2. Use cardinal directions (North, South, East, and West) to

    a. identify the directions from your town/city to Savannah: _____

    b. identify the directions from your town/city to Atlanta: _____

    c. identify the directions from your town/city to Columbus: _____

3. Use the letter/number grid to identify the location of

    a. your town/city: _____

    b. Atlanta: _____

    c. Savannah: _____

4. Use the map scale to determine the following distances

    a. your town/city to Atlanta: _____

    b. your town/city to Savannah: _____

    c. your town/city to Albany: _____

5. Now, presume that you are driving from your town to the following locations and must use the highways and interstates indicated on the map. Use the scale to measure road mileage and describe the route, e.g., Hwy 29 E to I-20. (You can use MapQuest to compare your route and mileage.)

    a. your town/city to Atlanta: _____

    b. your town/city to Savannah: _____

    c. your town/city to Albany: _____

Name_____   Date_____

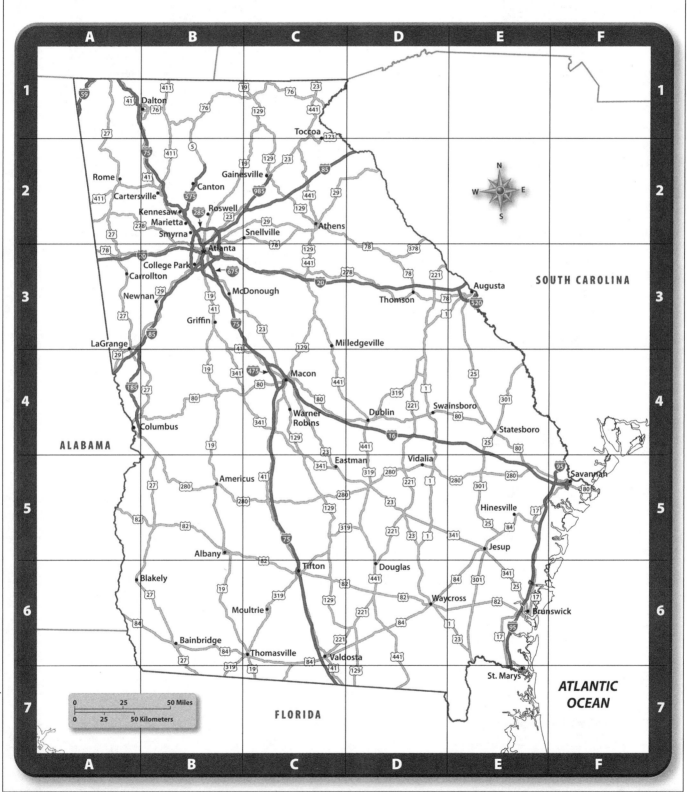

Name_____   **Date**_____

Evaluate the Preamble to the U.S. Constitution

Directions: Read the preamble to the U.S. Constitution and reword its key phrases in your own terms.

We the people of the United States, in order to form a more perfect union, establish justice, insure domestic tranquility, provide for the common defense, promote the general welfare, and secure the blessings of liberty to ourselves and our posterity, do ordain and establish this Constitution for the United States of America.

Define *preamble.* _____

_____

What the Preamble Says	What It Means to You
Establish justice	
Insure domestic tranquility	
Provide for common defense	
Promote the general welfare	
Secure blessings of liberty	

Name_____   **Date**_____

Compare the Preambles of the U.S. and Georgia Constitutions

Directions: Use your favorite search engine to locate the preamble of the Georgia constitution. Identify key themes and/or phrases in U.S. and Georgia preambles. List similarities in the boxes below and consider why the documents are alike in many ways.

U.S. Constitution Preamble Says...	**Georgia Constitution Preamble Says...**

Differentiation Option: Direct some students to do research on the authors of both documents. Look for similarities and differences in areas of education, background, birthplace, etc. Consider how the lives of the authors shaped the preambles.

Name_____ Date_____

Identify Georgia Voting Requirements

Directions: Review pages 62-66 to answer the questions below.

1. List the requirements to vote in Georgia:

   a. _____

   b. _____

   c. _____

2. When is the first governor's election in which you will be eligible to vote? (Georgia governors are elected in November of even years when there is *not* a presidential election: 2010, 2014, 2018, etc.)_____

3. List reasons why a citizen may not be able to vote:

   a. _____

   b. _____

4. Define *political party*. _____
   _____
   _____

5. What are the two major political parties in the United States and Georgia? _____
   _____
   _____

6. List some reasons why political parties are important. _____
   _____
   _____

7. How do political parties serve Georgians and U.S. citizens? _____
   _____
   _____

8. Discussion questions:

   a. How would politics in Georgia change if there were more than two major political parties?

   b. What are the pros and cons of having one political party dominate a state for an extended period?

Name_____ Date_____

Understand Voting Requirements in Georgia

Directions: In the boxes provided below, draw a picture that depicts each of the requirements to vote in Georgia. Be creative and have fun. See who can make the funniest, the best, or the most colorful drawings!

18 Years of Age	**United States Citizen**

Legal Resident of Georgia and the County Where You Will Vote

Differentiation Option: (1) Have students develop and defend an alternate set of voting requirements.
(2) Have students prioritize the current requirements and defend their assessment.

Name_____ Date_____

Vocabulary Crossword

Directions: Complete the crossword puzzle to test your vocabulary on this chapter.

Across

1. the fundamental plan of operation for a government
2. refusal to approve
4. to approve
5. system of government where people have the power, directly or indirectly
6. each branch of government has specific powers
7. an introductory statement
8. government system where elected leaders make decisions on behalf of the people
9. the basic plan for the United States government

Down

1. a system where one branch of government controls the powers of another
3. a two-house legislature

Differentiation Option: Have students prepare their own clue list based on a class-specific vocabulary list from this chapter.

Name_____ Date_____

Know Your State Legislature

Directions: Answer the questions below by circling **T** for True or **F** for False *before* reading from the textbook. Then, read the text to verify your answer. Write a brief quote from the book to support your answer. If you missed the question at first, simply change your answer and write a quote for support.

T F 1. The official name for the Georgia legislature is the Georgia Assembly.

_____

T F 2. The total membership of the legislature is 220 members.

_____

T F 3. House members in Georgia serve 2-year terms and state senators serve 4-year terms.

_____

T F 4. A person must be at least 25 years of age to serve in the House or Senate.

_____

T F 5. A candidate for the state legislature must be a U.S. citizen.

_____

T F 6. A candidate for the state legislature must be a resident of Georgia.

_____

T F 7. The Georgia legislature meets 100 days each year.

_____

T F 8. Every five years, the state counts its population and redraws district boundaries based on changes in population.

_____

Name_____ Date_____

House or Senate?

Directions: Read the statements below and write **H** if the statement pertains only to the organization of the House of Representatives and **S** if it pertains only to the organization of the Senate. If it pertains to both, write **H/S.**

_____ 1. The presiding officer of this chamber is chosen by its members.

_____ 2. The presiding officer can control debate in this chamber.

_____ 3. This chamber elects a president pro tempore.

_____ 4. Committee chairpersons are chosen by the speaker of this chamber.

_____ 5. The presiding officer does not vote in this chamber.

_____ 6. Committee chairpersons in this chamber are chosen by the lieutenant governor.

_____ 7. The presiding officer of this chamber can order a roll call vote on any issue.

_____ 8. The presiding officer of this chamber is the lieutenant governor.

_____ 9. This chamber has 36 standing committees.

_____ 10. This chamber elects a speaker pro tempore.

_____ 11. The presiding officer of this chamber could, under some circumstances, become the governor without being elected to that position.

_____ 12. This chamber has ad hoc committees.

_____ 13. This chamber has caucuses whose members meet to stay informed on issues.

_____ 14. This chamber has 26 standing committees.

_____ 15. This chamber takes part in conference committees.

_____ 16. The presiding officer of this chamber can make members attend sessions in order to have a quorum.

_____ 17. This chamber has 56 members.

_____ 18. The presiding officer of this chamber is called the speaker.

_____ 19. This chamber has interim study committees that work on issues before the session starts.

_____ 20. This chamber has 180 members.

Name_____   **Date**_____

Explain How a Bill Becomes a Law in Georgia

Directions: Before reading how a bill becomes a law, guess the correct order of steps in the process. Then, use the textbook to put the steps in the correct order.

Steps for a Bill to Become a Law	Your Guess of the Correct Order	Correct Order, Based on Reading the Textbook
Both houses approve the same version of the bill.		
Committee approves the bill and sends it to the floor for a vote.		
Bill is assigned to a committee for hearings.		
Bill is submitted, formatted, and given a number.		
After approval by the first house, bill is sent to the other house for committee and floor vote.		
Bill goes to the governor for action.		

Name_____   Date_____

Research a Recent Bill in Georgia

Directions: Use the Internet to track a bill as it moves through the Georgia General Assembly session. At home or in your school computer lab, go to **www.legis.ga.gov** and pick out a bill that interests you. Fill in the following information about the bill.

1. What is the number of the bill? _____

2. In which house was the bill introduced? _____

3. Who introduced the bill? _____

4. Write a brief summary of the bill. _____

   _____

   _____

5. What made you select this particular bill? _____

   _____

   _____

6. To which committee(s) was the bill assigned in each house? _____

   _____

7. Make notes of the day the bill was introduced, when it was read and voted on in each house, etc.

   _____

   _____

8. What is your opinion of the bill? Is it a good idea? How will it benefit the people of Georgia?

   How much do you think it will cost? _____

   _____

   _____

Differentiation Options: (1) Assign specific individuals or small groups to develop their own ideas for possible laws. (2) As a class or in small groups (subcommittees), debate the merits of the proposed bills.

Name_____ Date_____

Participate in Your Government

Directions: Think of a current law that should be deleted or changed, or think of an original idea for a law that you think should be adopted in Georgia. Write a short persuasive letter that describes the law and why you think it is needed. Go to **www.legis.ga.gov** and look up the name of your state representative and senator. Address your letter to those legislators.

_____
_____
_____
_____
_____
_____
_____
_____
_____
_____
_____
_____
_____
_____
_____
_____
_____
_____

Yours truly,

_____

Name_____   **Date**_____

Review State Government Terms

Directions: Match each term with the appropriate description or definition.

_____   1. a legislative committee that is present year to year   A. speaker of the House

_____   2. the presiding officer of the Georgia State Senate   B. lieutenant governor

_____   3. an informal group of the legislature   C. governor

_____   4. a group of legislators who study issues in between legislative sessions   D. caucus

_____   5. the presiding officer of the Georgia House of Representatives   E. General Assembly

_____   6. the chief executive officer of the state   F. standing committee

_____   7. the official name for the Georgia legislative branch   G. interim committee

_____   8. the process of identifying district size based on population   H. apportionment

Name_____ **Date**_____

The Executive Branch in Georgia's State Government

Directions: Answer the questions below by circling **T** for True or **F** for False *before* reading from the textbook. Then, read the text to verify your answer. Write a brief quote from the book to support your answer. If you missed the question at first, simply change your answer and write a quote for support.

T F   1. The governor is the chief executive of the state.

_____

T F   2. The governor commands the state militia.

_____

T F   3. The governor appoints the lieutenant governor.

_____

T F   4. The term of office for the governor is eight years.

_____

T F   5. The governor may serve up to three consecutive terms.

_____

T F   6. The candidate for governor must have a college degree.

_____

T F   7. The governor appoints the leaders of all state departments such as secretary of state.

_____

T F   8. The governor can force the legislature to hold special meetings.

_____

T F   9. It is possible for the governor and lieutenant governor to be from different parties.

_____

T F   10. The lieutenant governor is restricted to the same number of terms as the governor.

_____

Name_____　Date_____

Formal Powers of the Governor

Directions: The Georgia constitution defines several specific or "formal" powers for the governor. Read pages 92-94 about the formal powers. In the space provided, summarize these powers in your own words.

The Governor's Formal Powers	Your Summary/Description
Chief executive	
Chief law enforcement officer	
Commander-in-chief of state military forces	
Proposes an annual budget	
Appoints replacements for General Assembly or judicial offices	
Can call a special legislative session	
Appoints members to commissions/boards	

Name_____   **Date**_____

Bumper Stickers for Executive Issues

Directions: Think about and jot down issues that interest you or impact your life. List at least five items below. Then, in the space provided, develop a bumper sticker idea that would relay those thoughts or ideas to motorists. (Remember that clever and funny slogans will bring more attention to your cause!)

Issue	Bumper Sticker
1. _____ _____ _____	
2. _____ _____ _____	
3. _____ _____ _____	
4. _____ _____ _____	
5. _____ _____ _____	

Name_____   **Date**_____

Vocabulary of the Executive Branch

Directions: Match each term with the appropriate description or definition.

_____ 1. In this role, the governor performs ceremonial tasks, such as serving as spokesperson for the state.

A. commander-in-chief

_____ 2. This official maintains public records, archives, and documents.

B. formal powers

_____ 3. In this role, the governor commands the Georgia National Guard.

C. head of state

_____ 4. This official is selected in statewide voting and oversees our school systems.

D. constitutional officers

_____ 5. Georgia leaders try to encourage these business risk takers.

E. secretary of state

_____ 6. This official is the state's chief legal officer and head of the Department of Law.

F. attorney general

_____ 7. These are the heads of specifically designated executive departments who are chosen in statewide elections.

G. entrepreneurs

_____ 8. These powers are designated by the state constitution.

H. state school superintendent

Name_____   Date_____

Review the State Court System

Directions: In order to review and better understand the court system in Georgia, complete the chart below.

Type of Court	Where It is Found (State, County, City)	Typical Types of Cases in This Court
State Supreme Court (Tier 1)		
Court of Appeals (Tier 1)		
Superior Court (Tier 2)		
State Court (Tier 3)		
Probate Court (Tier 3)		
Magistrate Court (Tier 3)		
Juvenile Court (Tier 3)		
Municipal Court (Tier 3)		

Name_____   Date_____

Explain the Criminal Justice Process

Directions: Read about the three major steps in the criminal justice process on pages 120-123. In the spaces provided below, write a brief summary of each step. You may only use 40 words for each summary, so make every word count!

Step 1: Pretrial Proceedings

_____ _____ _____ _____ _____ _____ _____
_____ _____ _____ _____ _____ _____ _____
_____ _____ _____ _____ _____ _____ _____
_____ _____ _____ _____ _____ _____ _____
_____ _____ _____ _____ _____ _____ _____
_____ _____ _____ _____ _____ .

Step 2: The Trial

_____ _____ _____ _____ _____ _____ _____
_____ _____ _____ _____ _____ _____ _____
_____ _____ _____ _____ _____ _____ _____
_____ _____ _____ _____ _____ _____ _____
_____ _____ _____ _____ _____ _____ _____
_____ _____ _____ _____ _____ .

Step 3: The Appeal

_____ _____ _____ _____ _____ _____ _____
_____ _____ _____ _____ _____ _____ _____
_____ _____ _____ _____ _____ _____ _____
_____ _____ _____ _____ _____ _____ _____
_____ _____ _____ _____ _____ _____ _____
_____ _____ _____ _____ _____ .

Name_____ **Date**_____

Examine Current Court Cases in Georgia

Directions: Use your favorite search engine to find information about a current or recent significant court case in your city or region or in the state. Then, fill in the information below.

1. Summarize the key points of the case. _____
   _____
   _____
   _____
   _____
   _____

2. Which type of court heard the case, and who was the judge? _____
   _____
   _____
   _____

3. What was the decision of the judge or jury in the case? _____
   _____
   _____
   _____

4. If the defendant was found guilty, what was the punishment? _____
   _____
   _____
   _____

5. Does either side intend to appeal the case? If so, what type of court will handle the appeal? _____
   _____
   _____
   _____

Name_____   **Date**_____

Key Government Terms

Directions: Unscramble the words to complete the sentences.

1. An injury to society is known as a _____ . (rciem)

2. An individual who files a lawsuit is a _____ . (fianplfit)

3. A _____ (nolyef) is a very serious crime.

4. A minor crime, such as shoplifting, is known as a _____ . (demaenromis)

5. If a crime is committed, the case will be dealt with in a _____ (nacrmili) court.

6. In cases where no crime is committed, such as a divorce, a _____ (livic) court will hear the case.

7. The basic responsibility of courts is to _____ (idujadteac) matters, that is, to hear both sides and make a decision.

8. In a _____ (milrepnryai) hearing, a judge determines if there was a crime and whether or not _____ (bablerop) cause exists against a particular suspect.

9. During a trial, the individual charged with a crime is the _____ . (fenantedd)

10. A _____ (urjy) member is responsible for hearing the court case and making a verdict of guilt or innocence. During the trial, _____ (wsssitene) provide evidence.

Name_____   **Date**_____

Juvenile Delinquent, Unruly Child, or Deprived Child

Directions: Read each scenario below and indicate the status of the juvenile based on the description.

JD=Juvenile Delinquent   **UC**=Unruly Child   **DC**=Deprived Child

_____   1.   Individual runs away from home.

_____   2.   Child is routinely left unattended by parents.

_____   3.   Person is caught selling marijuana.

_____   4.   Individual uses false I.D. to buy beer.

_____   5.   Person is found in possession of alcohol.

_____   6.   Child is malnourished.

_____   7.   Child shows indications of physical abuse.

_____   8.   Individual shoplifts five music devices at a department store.

_____   9.   Individual is neglected.

_____   10. Individual uses a gun in an armed robbery.

_____   11. Child disobeys reasonable commands of parents.

_____   12. Individual goes to a place where alcohol is served without a parent.

_____   13. Individual has a false identification card in his/her possession.

Name_____   Date_____

Steps in the Juvenile Court System

Directions: Complete the chart below to review your understanding of the juvenile court system. Briefly summarize each step in the box.

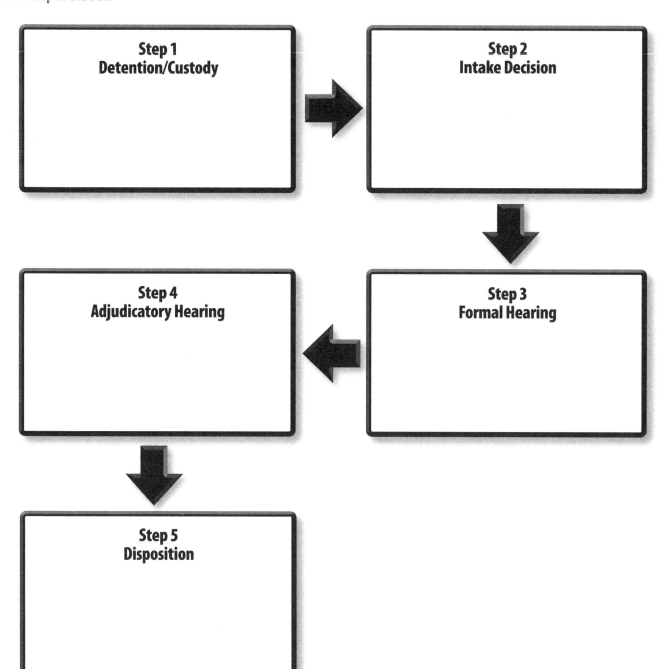

Step 1
Detention/Custody

Step 2
Intake Decision

Step 4
Adjudicatory Hearing

Step 3
Formal Hearing

Step 5
Disposition

Name_____   **Date**_____

Why Do We Have a Juvenile Justice System?

Because Georgia and other states recognize that juveniles deserve the best opportunity possible to become productive members of society, many resources are applied to the juvenile court system to achieve this goal.

Directions: Read Section 2 in your textbook and the following quote from the Georgia Department of Juvenile Justice home page. Then, fill in the information below.

> *While rehabilitation of these youths is our primary goal, public safety for the citizens of Georgia is paramount, and juvenile crime must not detract from this. We must not take for granted the many victims of juvenile crime and potential victims who deserve a better quality of life for themselves and their families.*
>
> *Here at the Department of Juvenile Justice, we believe these youths need every opportunity to turn their lives around and become productive citizens. It is our belief that given the right kind of attention and treatment, many of these youngsters can be redirected and that there is hope for them.*

1. Explain why Georgia has established a special system for juvenile offenders. _____
   _____
   _____

2. Discuss how Georgia tries to balance the rights of victims with the need to help juveniles. _____
   _____
   _____

3. Explain why certain offenses committed by juveniles automatically warrant consideration for punishment as an
   adult. _____
   _____

4. One significant difference between adult and juvenile trial cases is the absence of a jury for juveniles. Explain why
   you believe the juvenile does not have a jury and whether or not you think this is a good policy. _____
   _____
   _____
   _____

Name_____   **Date**_____

Discuss Ways to Avoid Juvenile Delinquency

Directions: After reading this chapter, you should have a good understanding of how the juvenile court system in Georgia is organized. Most young people in Georgia will never experience the system from the inside. Think about practical ways that you and your friends can avoid trouble. Prepare for a class discussion by listing three things you can do to avoid trouble.

1. _____

_____

_____

2. _____

_____

_____

3. _____

_____

_____

Directions: After writing your ideas, share them with your classmates. In the space below, take notes during the discussion. Write down the best ideas you hear.

NOTES: _____

_____

_____

_____

_____

_____

_____

_____

_____

_____

_____

Name_____ **Date**_____

Juvenile Courts in Georgia

Directions: Read the chapter opener on page 127. Summarize the reasons why the juvenile justice system was established. _____

_____

_____

Directions: Match each term with the appropriate description or definition.

_____ 1. a crime for which the punishment is 12 months in prison, life imprisonment, or death

_____ 2. lawbreaking by persons under the age of 17

_____ 3. a child who commits acts that would not be offenses if committed by adults

_____ 4. a minor who is without adequate food, shelter, or protection

_____ 5. a crime for which the sentence is 12 months in prison or less

_____ 6. someone under 17 years old who has committed a delinquent act and is considered to need treatment

_____ 7. a citizen age 17 or younger

A. juvenile

B. felony

C. misdemeanor

D. delinquent act

E. unruly child

F. deprived child

G. juvenile delinquent

Directions: Give examples of the following:

Unruly Behavior	**Delinquent Behaviors**

Directions: On a separate sheet of paper, in your own words, write a paragraph explaining why you think the juvenile court system is important.

Name_____ Date_____

How Much Do You Know About Your County?

Directions: It is important that you are well acquainted with your own county. Let's see how well you do in describing your county in words and graphics.

1. Write a short descriptive paragraph describing your home county. Don't forget to include the name of your county and its county seat. Be sure to include the geographic features, demographic aspects, historic sites, parks, and recreational facilities that other counties may not have. Also mention your climate, your local industries, and your largest businesses. Finally, tell where your county is located in the state and how to get there if someone wants to visit.

_____

_____

_____

_____

_____

_____

_____

_____

_____

_____

_____

_____

2. Draw a map of your county. Label the cities and towns, geographic features such as mountains or rivers, state and federal historic sites, and parks.

Name_____   **Date**_____

Compare Types of City Governments

Directions: Review the different types of city governments. Use the chart below to review how important roles and tasks are allocated to the different leaders. Note that the Role of Manager is only applicable to the Council-Manager form of government.

	Strong Mayor-Council	**Weak Mayor-Council**	**Council-Manager**
Role of Mayor			
Role of Manager	Not Applicable	Not Applicable	
Special Powers of Mayor or Manager			
Role of Council			

Directions: Research your city government or the nearest city government and answer the following:

1. What is the name of the city you researched? _____

2. Who is the current mayor and when was he or she elected? _____

_____

3. What form of government does the city have? _____

Name_____   **Date**_____

Who Provides Your Local Services?

Directions: Depending on where you live, either the city or county provides many services to you and your family. Using this simple list of services and your favorite search engine, identify who provides these services to your home. Keep in mind that there may be differences among students in your class, depending on where the students live.

Name the city or county that provides these services:

Police Protection: _____

Fire Protection: _____

Ambulance: _____

Animal Control: _____

Water Utilities: _____

Garbage Collection: _____

Parks: _____

Libraries: _____

Public Transportation: _____

Schools: _____

Directions: Explain why services in many areas are shared responsibilities between city and county providers.

_____

_____

_____

_____

Name_____ Date_____

Design a Poster for Your City or Area

Directions: Your task is to design a poster that highlights the positive aspects of your city or the area where you live. The poster should emphasize positive features such as parks and recreation activities, job opportunities, and the services provided by your city—or the county if you live in an unincorporated area. Make your poster fun and inviting for people who might want to visit or live in your area.

Name_____   **Date**_____

Vocabulary Matching

Directions: Match each term with the appropriate description or definition. Then, answer the questions below regarding your own town or city.

_____   1. the location where an individual can conduct transactions, such as paying a tax, with their local government

_____   2. the local governmental district that Georgia and most states are divided into

_____   3. the process in which cities and counties share responsibility for providing services

_____   4. the written document that allows a municipality to exist and function

_____   5. the part of a county that is not within any city boundary

_____   6. another name for a city

A. county

B. charter (origins)

C. county seat

D. unincorporated area

E. municipality

F. intergovernmental cooperation

7. What is the name of the city/county where you live? _____

8. Who provides your police protection? _____

9. Who provides your fire protection? _____

10. Who supports your nearest public library? _____

11. Is your school system supported by county or city? _____

12. Who supports the nearest park to your home? _____

Name_____   **Date**_____

Who Were the Early Peoples?

Directions: Review the critical information regarding the peoples of each era. Using that information, complete the chart below by filling the blocks with the requested information.

	Time Period	Food Sources	Tools	Types of Shelters
Paleo				
Archaic				
Woodland				
Mississippian				

Name_____ Date_____

Identify the Correct Era

Directions: Based on your reading about the different groups of early peoples, identify the group that is *most* associated with each item below. Place a letter in the blank to indicate the era you believe is correct.

P=Paleo   **A**=Archaic   **W**=Woodland   **M**=Mississippian

_____   1.   Improved tools and had spear points

_____   2.   Developed more permanent settlements that included circular houses

_____   3.   Began to plant and harvest crops

_____   4.   Lived in small groups of 20-50 people

_____   5.   Most complex societies that existed in this time frame

_____   6.   Nomadic wanderers in search of food

_____   7.   Known for large burial grounds

_____   8.   Changed their diet from large to small game

_____   9.   The oldest group

_____   10.   Developed the largest group of villages

_____   11.   Would have enjoyed mammoth "burgers"

_____   12.   Developed axes and drills

_____   13.   Developed the bow and arrow

_____   14.   First to make pottery

_____   15.   Societal structure allowed the rise of powerful chiefs

_____   16.   Corn, squash, and pumpkins were regular food items

_____   17.   Built towns fortified with palisades

_____   18.   Made objects with copper

_____   19.   Encountered the first Spanish explorers

Name_____   Date_____

Motivations of European Explorers

Directions: After reading pages 172-175 in your textbook, read the following statements. Circle **T** if you think a statement is true and **F** is you think it is false. Next, review the textbook and write a brief quote to support your answer. Be ready to defend your answer with other students in the class.

T F 1. One reason that Europeans began to explore far from their boundaries was to expand their trading relationships with Middle Eastern and Italian merchants._____

_____

_____

T F 2. The monarchs of Europe were motivated to pay for voyages in their hopes of increasing their own wealth, territories, and power. _____

_____

_____

T F 3. The idea of spreading Christianity was not an important part of the age of exploration. _____

_____

_____

T F 4. After the New World was discovered, many new crops and raw materials were brought to Europe, but few, if any, items were exchanged from Europe to the New World. _____

_____

T F 5. The Europeans brought new diseases to the peoples of the New World, but they quickly developed immunities. _____

_____

_____

Name_____   Date_____

De Soto's Exploration of Georgia

Directions: Imagine you are one of de Soto's solders as you explore the area we now know as Georgia. In the space provided next to the pictures, write a Facebook posting as if you were telling your friends back home what they are missing.

1. _____
   _____
   _____
   _____
   _____
   _____
   _____
   _____

2. _____
   _____
   _____
   _____
   _____
   _____
   _____
   _____
   _____

3. Given that the purpose of de Soto's exploration was the discovery of gold and riches, would you describe his expedition as a success or failure? Why? _____
   _____
   _____
   _____
   _____
   _____

Name_____   **Date**_____

The Europeans Arrive

Directions: Imagine that you are a Native American living in Georgia at the time of de Soto's exploration. You are out hunting for deer and have just stumbled upon the scene in the picture below. Write a note describing the scene so your friend can relay the message back to the village. (Remember, you've never seen a white man or any of the items they wear or carry. Consider any possible threat or possibility of trading as you write.)

_____

_____

_____

_____

_____

_____

_____

_____

_____

_____

Name_____   Date_____

Vocabulary Scramble

Directions: Unscramble the words to complete the sentences. Be sure to capitalize the vocabulary words where appropriate.

1.   Manmade items such as pottery and tools that provide clues to early people are called
     _____. (trifaatcs)

2.   The study of artifacts is _____. (haoalorecgy)

3.   A set of beliefs, traditions, and way of life for a group of people is its _____. (tulruec)

4.   _____(nadsmo) are groups of people who wander from place to place.

5.   The earliest group of cultures in Georgia was the _____ (laoep) culture.

6.   The Native American group credited with development of pottery was the _____.
     (chacrai) culture.

7.   The most advanced group of early peoples with extended societies and large burial mounds was the
     _____ (ppssssiiiiman) culture.

8.   The _____ (dandolwo) culture was the early peoples credited with the development of
     the bow and arrow.

9.   The practice of planting and harvesting food-producing plants is called
     _____. (tictlurohreu)

10. A _____ (liasdaep) is a series of sharpened poles used to provide security around a
     settlement.

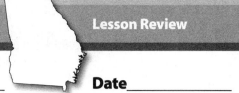

Name_____   **Date**_____

Explain the Charter of 1732

Directions: Use the information on page 191 to learn about the charter that helped establish the colony.

1. Define *charter*. _____

2. In your own words, describe what the charter did. _____
   _____

3. Write the motto that was adopted by the trustees, and explain what you think it meant to them.
   (It may help to refer back to the reasons the charter was established.) _____
   _____

4. In whose honor was the colony named? _____

5. How long did the charter grant control of the colony to the trustees? _____

6. Why do you suppose there were a defined number of years for trustee control? _____
   _____
   _____

7. What limit was placed on making laws? _____

8. Why do you think the king imposed the limit? _____
   _____

9. How did the trustees work around this limitation? _____
   _____

10. The charter prevented the trustees from making any profit from the colony. How do you believe this restriction
    is related to the reasons for establishing the colony and to the motto? _____
    _____

11. A charter is essentially a legal contract between two groups of people—in this case, the trustees
    and the king. Name a few examples of similar agreements used in our lives today. _____
    _____

Name_____ Date_____

Prepare to Negotiate

Directions: Imagine that you are Oglethorpe or Tomochichi. Tomorrow, you will meet to negotiate cooperation in the Georgia colony. Consider the important issues facing your people. What do you have to offer the other man, and what do you want him to provide? Think about your trading situation, security issues, and any rules that you might need to impose on either or both sides. List your ideas and then pair up with your opposite number to negotiate the establishment of the colony.

	Oglethorpe	Tomochichi
Rules		
Security		
Trade		

Name_____   **Date**_____

Life in Early Georgia

Directions: Read pages 195-196 and pages 208-210, which describe the hard work and dangers that faced the colonists. Imagine you are one of the first colonists, recently arrived in Savannah. The ship *Ann* is leaving soon, and you want to send a quick letter to your family. Use the outline below to finish your letter.

Dear _____,

    We have recently landed and the weather is _____,
and the water is _____.

    I visited the sick yesterday and saw _____

_____.

    As far as the work goes, I spend most of my time _____.
I also work at _____.

    I am building a house and it will be _____.
In my garden I am planting _____.

    Something really funny happened the other day when _____

_____. I saw my first Indian
just yesterday, and he was _____.

    So far, I think Mr. Oglethorpe _____

_____.

    In conclusion, life here is _____

_____

_____.

                     Your devoted _____,

Name_____ **Date**_____

Evaluating Primary Documents

Directions: Pick any one of the people in the picture below. Imagine what that person must be thinking while posing for the painting and observing the representatives of the other culture. Write a description of the scene from the standpoint of that person. (Ideas to consider include technology, education, culture, dress, language, and religion.)

_____

_____

_____

_____

_____

_____

_____

_____

_____

_____

Name_____   **Date**_____

New Settlers Arrive

Directions: For the colony to succeed, Oglethorpe needed more colonists to settle and establish farms. Over time, groups of colonists, both invited and uninvited, began to arrive. Read pages 201-202. Use the information to identify key summary notes about each group of new colonists. There should be at least two to three notes per group. Then, answer the question below.

	Summary Notes
Jews	
Salzburgers	
Highland Scots	
Moravians	

What were some challenges for Oglethorpe in trying to integrate people from so many different backgrounds and

religions? _____

_____

_____

_____

Name_____   Date_____

Leaders of the Trustee Era

Directions: Identify the individual or group based on each one's role in the trustee period.

_____   1. widely recognized as the man responsible for the establishment of the Georgia colony

_____   2. the group of men who worked together to establish the colony

_____   3. the colonists who gradually became dissatisfied with life in Georgia and with some of the trustees' rules

_____   4. the group of settlers recruited by Oglethorpe who settled the town of Darien

_____   5. settlers who established the town of Ebenezer and New Ebenezer and were opponents of slavery

_____   6. a group of settlers opposed by some trustees, but welcomed by Oglethorpe, who brought a much needed doctor to the colony

_____   7. a Yamacraw chief who welcomed the colonists and became a lifelong friend of Oglethorpe

_____   8. served as an interpreter for Oglethorpe and the Native Americans

_____   9. one of the groups that Oglethorpe and the trustees hoped to settle in the new colony

_____   10. person who granted the charter to the trustees and for whom the colony is named

A. trustees

B. Salzbergers

C. Jews

D. James Oglethorpe

E. Mary Musgrove

F. King George II

G. debtors

H. malcontents

I. Tomochichi

J. Highland Scots

Name_____ **Date**_____

Colonization Vocabulary Crossword

Directions: Use the clues below to complete the crossword puzzle. Try it first without using your textbook or notebooks.

Across

3. the first city established in Georgia
4. the ship that carried the first colonists
5. the native tribe led by Tomochichi
7. an organization that helped ensure the security of the new colony
9. legal agreement that established the guidelines for starting the Georgia colony
10. colonists known for their growing unhappiness about the situation in the colony

Down

1. individuals who convinced King George to allow them to establish the colony
2. individuals who contracted themselves to work for a certain number of years before gaining their freedom
6. the key leader in establishing the colony
7. the person who served as interpreter for Tomochichi and Oglethorpe
8. an idea under which Great Britain hoped to export goods that were more valuable than those they imported

Name_____ **Date**_____

Royal Governors Change the Colony

Directions: After the trustee period, Georgia became a royal colony. The royal governors implemented many changes in the way the colony was governed. Read pages 216-217 to understand some of the changes implemented by the governors and summarize them in your own words.

1. List some of the specific powers given to the governor by the king. _____
   _____
   _____
   _____

2. How many men served on the Governor's Council? _____

3. What roles did the Governor's Council play? _____
   _____
   _____

4. Which government body was elected? _____

5. What roles did the Commons House of Assembly serve? _____
   _____

6. What were the eligibility requirements for election to the Commons House of Assembly? _____
   _____

7. What were the requirements for voting? _____
   _____

8. In your own words, summarize how this new involvement in colonial government must have changed Georgia.
   _____
   _____
   _____

9. Discussion question: Under the trustees, Georgia colonists had little influence on the rules of the colony. As you see in this reading, the royal governors opened the door for individual participation in government. How do you think these changes may have actually played a role in the coming war for independence?

Name_____ **Date**_____

Compare Royal Governors

Directions: Use the information on pages 220-224 to fill in the chart. Explore the key achievements and contributions of each governor.

	When He Served	Key Accomplishments
John Reynolds		
Henry Ellis		
James Wright		

Name_____ **Date**_____

Compare and Contrast Royal and Trustee Eras

Directions: Use your knowledge of the trustee and royal colony eras to compare and contrast key aspects of colonial government.

	Trustee Period	Royal Colony Period
Who Ran the Colony and Under What Authority		
Land Ownership Policies		
Slavery Policy		

Name_____   Date_____

Vocabulary Matching

Directions: After reading this chapter, complete the matching questions below to review important terms, events, and people.

_____   1. Tar and pitch are examples of this important Georgia export.

_____   2. He was the first royal governor.

_____   3. He was the second royal governor.

_____   4. Passed in 1775, it required 16- to 60-year-old men to enroll.

_____   5. This group of new colonists, originally from New England, moved to Georgia from South Carolina.

_____   6. This series of laws was passed to manage the control of slaves.

_____   7. This future U.S. president was partly responsible for starting the French and Indian War.

_____   8. He served as the third and final royal governor.

_____   9. This was one method of granting land to colonists during the royal era.

_____   10. This very religious group of colonists believed all persons possessed a spark of God, or "inner light."

_____   11. This was the location of the Council House and the seat of government for Royal Georgia.

A. John Reynolds

B. Militia Act

C. George Washington

D. Henry Ellis

E. Savannah

F. James Wright

G. naval stores

H. headright system

I. Puritans

J. Quakers

K. slave code

Name_____   Date_____

French and Indian War Contributes to the American Revolution

Directions: Review pages 247-248 concerning the effects of the French and Indian War, then fill in the chart below.

Effect of the French and Indian War	Impact on the Colonies
Britain needed money to pay off war debt.	
Britain began to enforce Navigation Acts.	
British soldiers stayed in the colonies after the war.	
The French were removed from the Ohio River Valley and the Spanish were removed from Florida.	

Name_____   Date_____

Meet With the Sons of Liberty!

Directions: Make a poster or flyer that you will post in your own town or village for the Sons of Liberty. It must include the following: why you should join, a meeting place and time, and a motto for your group.

Name_____   **Date**_____

Report from Tondee's Tavern

Directions: Imagine you are a news reporter witnessing a Sons of Liberty meeting at Tondee's Tavern. Write notes for your report. Do not take sides; simply think about the issues and what the attendees would have discussed. Think about the arguments on both sides of these issues.

(Here are some ideas to get you started: (1) What kind of people make up the group? Are they farmers or more of the upper class? (2) How might the attendees be torn between being loyal subjects of the king yet, at the same time, beginning to feel separate from Britain?)

_____

_____

_____

_____

_____

_____

_____

_____

_____

_____

_____

_____

_____

_____

_____

_____

_____

_____

_____

_____

_____

_____

_____

Name_____   Date_____

Timeline of Key Events Leading to the Revolution

Directions: In the space before each event, indicate the year when it took place. Then place these key events on the timeline.

_____   Tea Act

_____   First Continental Congress

_____   Sugar Act

_____   Stamp Act

_____   Sons of Liberty established in Georgia

_____   Declaration of Independence

_____   Townshend Revenue Act

_____   Intolerable Acts

1760   **1765**   **1770**   **1780**

Name_____   **Date**_____

Toward a Revolution

Directions: Match the following vocabulary terms with their correct definitions.

_____   1. The first of many new taxes that angered colonists

_____   2. Placed a tax on all printed items and documents

_____   3. Taxed items imported into the colonies such as glass, paint,
                and tea

_____   4. A move by Britain that gave one company a monopoly on a
                favorite beverage

_____   5. A refusal to buy goods from a specific business or company,
                usually associated with a type of protest

_____   6. The boundary established after the French and Indian War

_____   7. A British action that forced colonists to host soldiers in their
                homes and that closed the port of Boston

_____   8. A meeting that resulted in the establishment of a boycott of
                British goods

_____   9. A meeting that resulted in the Declaration of Independence

_____   10. A motto the colonists used to describe the new taxes

_____   11. A term the British used to describe their right to tax the
                colonists

A. boycott

B. First Continental Congress

C. virtual representation

D. Tea Act

E. Second Continental Congress

F. Sugar Act

G. Proclamation Line of 1763

H. Stamp Act

I. Intolerable Acts

J. taxation without representation

K. Townshend Revenue Act

Name_____   Date_____

Examine the Georgia Constitution of 1777

Directions: Using the information on pages 277-278, describe on the chart below how the Georgia Constitution of 1777 dealt with key issues.

Issue	What Did the Constitution Say?
Naming of the first eight counties	
County role in local government	
Who could vote	
What were requirements for holding office	
What type of legislature	
Who elected the governor and his council	
Governor's powers and his term of office	
Religion	

Name_____   Date_____

Construct a Timeline of Key Events

Directions: Identify the month and year that each of the key events below took place. Then use that list to make a time-line of key revolutionary events in Georgia.

1776	**1777**	**1778**	**1779**	**1780**	**1781**	**1782**

Month/Year

_____   Declaration of Independence arrives in Georgia

_____   Battle of the Rice Boats

_____   Battle of Kettle Creek

_____   French and Georgia militia attempt to retake Savannah

_____   British are defeated at Yorktown

_____   British capture Savannah

_____   Georgia ratifies its first temporary constitution, "The Rules and Regulations…"

_____   British leave Savannah

Name_____ **Date**_____

Design a Georgia Historical Marker

Directions: You have probably seen historical markers along the roadside as you drive around Georgia. This is your chance to design your own marker. Choose one of the key topics listed below (or a topic assigned by your teacher) and write an appropriate summary for a historical marker. Make sure you include vital information such as who, what, where, and significance of the person or event.

◆ Siege of Savannah ◆ Battle of Kettle Creek ◆ Elijah Clarke ◆ Austin Dabney ◆ Nancy Hart

Name_____   **Date**_____

Review Important Vocabulary from the Revolution

Directions: Use the clues below to complete the crossword puzzle and review important vocabulary terms and people from this chapter.

Across

6. Patriots who demanded the least amount of democratic changes
8. a frontier woman who is credited with killing Loyalists at her home
9. a battle with a militia victory that boosted the morale of those who wanted independence
10. a slave who fought with the colonists against the British

Down

1. citizen volunteers who served as soldiers when called upon
2. title given to those colonists who remained loyal to the King
3. Patriots who demanded the most drastic changes
4. an important Georgia city that was under siege by the British for much of the war
5. members of the British Parliament who supported the colonies' side
7. one of the key militia leaders at the Battle of Kettle Creek

Name_____   Date_____

Weaknesses of the Articles of Confederation

Directions: Read page 297 to learn about the Articles of Confederation. Then, fill in the chart below. You will find out later in the chapter if your predictions came true.

Weakness	Explain in Your Own Words	Predict Why This Weakness Might Be a Problem
No separate executive branch		
No national court system		
No power to tax		
Requirement for unanimous votes		

Name_____   Date_____

Explore Changes in Georgia in the Post-Revolutionary Era

Directions: Answer the questions below by circling **T** for True or **F** for False. Write a brief quote from the book to support your answer. Be prepared to discuss your answers and supporting quotes with your classmates.

The Economy:

T F 1. After the American Revolution, Georgia transformed its economy to an industrial base._____
_____
_____

T F 2. Many large cities were established. _____
_____
_____

Education:

T F 3. Georgia recognized the need for education and established free public schools for students. _____
_____
_____

T F 4. The University of Georgia became the first state-sponsored university in the nation._____
_____
_____

Religion:

T F 5. Churches remained racially separated after the Revolution._____
_____
_____

T F 6. With the defeat of the Loyalists, the religious scene in Georgia was reduced to one or two primary denominations._____
_____
_____

Differentiation Idea: Have students read and answer the questions True or False before reading the textbook. Next, have them search the text for supporting quotes to determine the accuracy of their guesses. If they guessed wrong before reading, have them make notes and simply change their answers accordingly.

Name_____   **Date**_____

What Was the Constitutional Convention All About?

Directions: Read/review pages 311-315 and fill in the information below concerning key aspects of the Constitutional Convention.

1. When and where did the Constitutional Convention meet? _____
    _____

2. Which state did not attend the convention? _____

3. Who were the four men who represented Georgia at the convention? _____
    _____

4. According to the textbook, the major problems with the Articles of Confederation were all related to what?
    _____

5. Describe the basic points of the Virginia Plan. _____
    _____
    _____
    _____

6. What were some of the complaints of the small states regarding the Virginia Plan? ___
    _____
    _____

7. In your own words, describe the Great Compromise. _____
    _____
    _____
    _____

8. What did the convention want in the executive branch? _____
    _____
    _____

9. Describe the judicial branch as established in the Constitution. _____
    _____
    _____

10. Which representatives from Georgia signed the Constitution? When? _____
    _____

Name_____ Date_____

Georgians Ratify the U.S. Constitution

Directions: Why did Americans choose to ratify the Constitution? We know that the Articles of Confederation were severely flawed. The Constitution addressed many of the shortcomings of the Articles. Review information in the chapter, and write notes that explain how the Constitution addressed each issue.

How did it appeal to states that had potential conflicts with Native Americans?

What was the Virginia Plan?

How many states had to ratify the Constitution before it became law?

What three branches of government were established?

Name_____   Date_____

Vocabulary Crossword Puzzle

Directions: Use the clues below to complete the crossword puzzle and review key terms from this chapter.

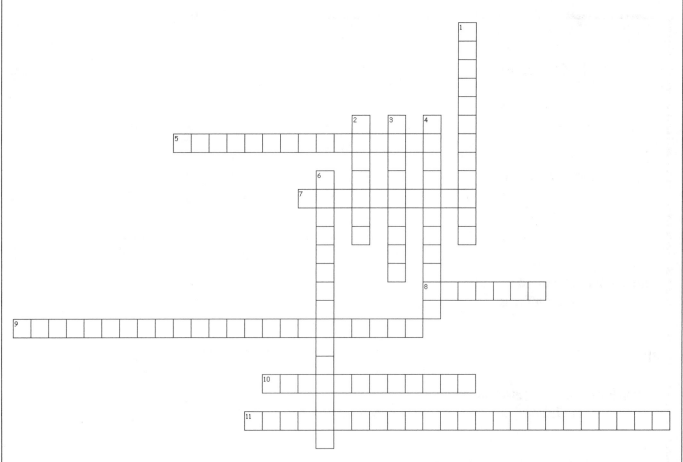

Across

5. agreement at the Constitutional Convention that established a bicameral legislature
7. one-house (legislature)
8. a fee for instruction
9. first United States constitution
10. public approval; usually associated with government actions such as a constitutional amendment
11. meeting of states in 1787 intended to improve the Articles of Confederation

Down

1. the plan introduced at the Constitutional Convention to replace the Articles of Confederation
2. primary cash crop immediately after the Revolution
3. two-house (legislature)
4. those who supported the new U.S. Constitution
6. those who opposed the new U.S. Constitution

Name_____ Date_____

Examine the Yazoo Land Fraud

Directions: Read pages 328-330 and fill in the chart below.

Role of land companies	
Which governor signed the act	
What conflict of interest existed for the elected officials	
What happened in the election of 1795	
What was the "fire brought down from heaven"	
In 1802, what happened to the western lands that were formerly part of Georgia	

Name_____ Date_____

Land Distribution in Georgia

Directions: Compare and contrast the headright system and land lottery.

	Headright System	**Land Lottery**
Began when		
Who was eligible		
How much land could they get		

Explain why selling land cheaply was a good idea for Georgia. _____
_____
_____
_____
_____

Name_____   Date_____

Compare the Economy and Technology in Georgia Between Eras

Directions: Fill in the chart below to compare technology and the economy between eras. Your teacher may also choose to facilitate a class discussion comparing information on this chart to the economy of Georgia today.

	Woodland/Mississippian Era	Post-Revolutionary Era
Crops		
Agricultural tools		
Transport technology		
Industry		

Name_____   **Date**_____

War of 1812

Directions: Find out about America's second war for independence by researching the War of 1812 in your textbook and online at **www.history.com/topics/war-of-1812**. Then, fill in the following information.

1. List causes of the War of 1812. _____

_____

_____

2. List the places in the United States where battles took place. _____

_____

_____

3. What was Georgia's role in the war? _____

_____

_____

4. What was the final outcome of the war? _____

_____

_____

5. Why do you think the war is "forgotten"? _____

_____

_____

6. What are some reasons it should NOT be forgotten? _____

_____

_____

Name_____   **Date**_____

Removal of Native Peoples

Directions: Review pages 344-349 to identify the key people and events associated with Indian removal.

1. An important leader of the Creek Indians, _____ was the son of a Scottish father and Creek mother.

2. Future president _____ gained some fame during fighting with the Red Stick Indians at Horseshoe Bend.

3. The first and second treaties of _____ were part of the gradual process of Native Americans losing their lands in Georgia.

4. Chief _____ was killed by his own people for agreeing to give away their lands without their approval.

5. _____ was the Cherokee credited with developing a written language for this people, known as a _____.

6. The Supreme Court ruled that the Cherokee land was not subject to Georgia law in the _____ case.

7. _____ was an important leader for the Cherokee Indians. His father was Scottish and his mother was Cherokee.

8. The Cherokee published their own newspaper known as the _____, printed in English and Cherokee.

9. Indicators of how the Cherokee adopted some aspects of white culture are reflected in their adoption of a constitution as well as establishing a capital city at _____.

10. One key event in Georgia that added tension to relations between whites and Indians was the discovery of _____ near _____ in the year _____.

11. Pressure to remove Indians from their homeland reached a peak when the United States Congress passed the _____ Act in the year _____.

12. This act set aside western lands in present-day _____ for Cherokee to move to.

13. The forced movement of the Cherokee westward is known as the _____.

Name_____ Date_____

On the Trail of Tears

Directions: Pick a person or animal in the picture below. Use your imagination and sensory perceptions to imagine what the Trail of Tears must have been like.

The person or animal I chose was _____
_____

With my eyes, I see _____
_____

With my nose, I smell _____
_____

With my ears, I hear _____
_____

With my hands, I feel _____
_____

With my mouth, I taste _____
_____

Differentiation Idea: Students may write a short story or poem about the Trail of Tears.

Name_____   **Date**_____

A Slave's Life

Directions: Pages 356-362 describe some of the key aspects of daily slave life. Read or review these pages and follow the steps below.

A good way to think about history is to try to visualize a particular event and imagine what a person truly experienced. After reviewing Section 1, Slavery in Georgia, imagine the experience of a slave.

1. Briefly describe your condition, e.g., I am a young female field hand who lives on a large plantation. _____
    _____

2. Fill in the chart below to tell about your sensory experience.

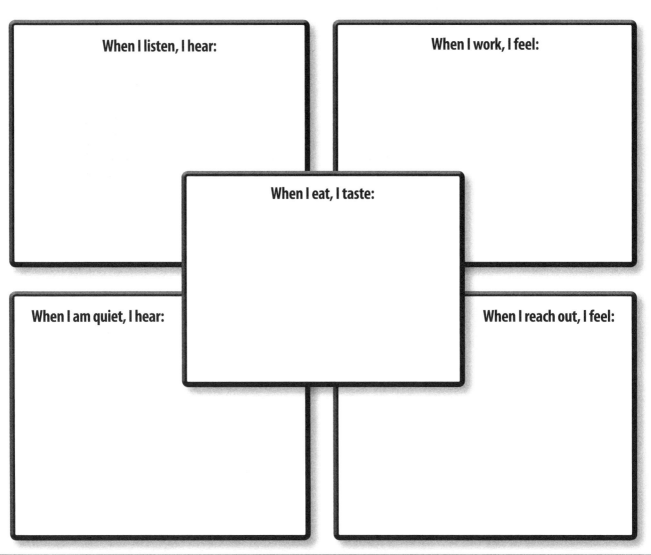

When I listen, I hear:

When I work, I feel:

When I eat, I taste:

When I am quiet, I hear:

When I reach out, I feel:

Name_____ Date_____

Understanding the Missouri Compromise

Directions: Use the map below to show the impact of the Missouri Compromise. Make a key for your map that shows what the colors represent.

1. Color code Missouri as a slave state.

2. Color code Maine as a free state.

3. Draw a line marking the 36°30' parallel.

4. Color code the area of the Louisiana Purchase that could not be slave (north of 36°30' and west to the Rocky Mountains).

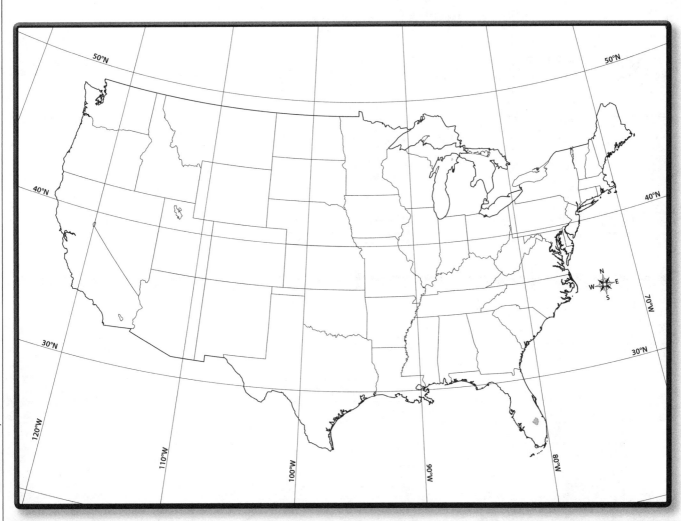

Name_____   Date_____

Taking Perspective on Antebellum Events

As events leading to the Civil War unfolded, there were many attempts to keep both sides of the slavery issue satisfied. Eventually, the South was convinced that the North intended to end slavery and violate the southern belief in states' rights.

Directions: Use the chart below to build a writing situation concerning antebellum events. Based on the framework you select, use the space below to draft an outline of your writing. Complete your writing on a separate piece of paper.

Role	Audience	Format	Topic
Slave in the South	Family member in another part of the country	Letter	Abolition and ending slavery
Southern slave owner	President or another politician	Newspaper report	Supporting slavery
Abolitionist	Newspaper reader	Poem	States' rights
Free black living in the North	A friend who is in your same position (role)	Diary entry	Missouri Compromise

Draft or outline your writing here:

_____
_____
_____
_____
_____
_____
_____
_____
_____
_____

Name_____   Date_____

Timeline of Key Antebellum Events

Directions: Identify the year that each of the events below took place. Then, use that list to make a timeline of key events in the antebellum period.

_____ Georgia passes new slave codes   _____ Compromise of 1850

_____ Missouri Compromise   _____ *Dred Scott* case reaches Supreme Court

_____ Kansas-Nebraska Act   _____ Mexican-American War begins

_____ Nullification crisis   _____ *Uncle Tom's Cabin* published

_____ Lincoln elected   _____ Nat Turner's slave revolt

| 1820 | 1830 | 1840 | 1850 | 1860 |

Differentiation Idea: After constructing the timeline, have students put the events in the order of their contribution to the Civil War.

Name_____   **Date**_____

React to Antebellum Events

Directions: Read the statements and circle whether you agree or disagree. In the space provided, write a short explanation for your choice.

1. The antebellum era is the time when the Civil War was fought.	Agree/Disagree:_____ _____ _____
2. There were few attempts to prevent the Civil War.	Agree/Disagree:_____ _____ _____
3. Sectionalism was a belief in supporting slavery.	Agree/Disagree:_____ _____ _____
4. Manifest destiny was the belief that the United States should be larger.	Agree/Disagree:_____ _____ _____
5. Under popular sovereignty, slaves were allowed to sue for freedom in courts.	Agree/Disagree:_____ _____ _____
6. Under the Missouri Compromise, a balance of free and slave states was maintained.	Agree/Disagree:_____ _____ _____
7. The Georgia Platform urged southern states to secede as soon as possible.	Agree/Disagree:_____ _____ _____
8. After the election of 1860, southern states began to secede.	Agree/Disagree:_____ _____ _____

Teacher Suggestion: Use this prior to beginning the chapter to pique interest and gauge knowledge. Direct students to circle Agree/Disagree at the beginning of class. After completion of your lesson, have them confirm their answers and write short comments.

Name_____   Date_____

Vocabulary Word Search

Directions: Identify the terms below from Chapter 15 and write them in the blanks provided. Then, find the terms in the puzzle below.

1. _____ Georgia laws concerning slavery
2. _____ Period before the Civil War
3. _____ Emphasis on one region over another
4. _____ Tax on goods shipped into a country from another country
5. _____ To void a federal law that a state believes is unconstitutional
6. _____ To withdraw from the United States
7. _____ Belief that the United States was bound to expand to the Pacific Ocean
8. _____ Allowed the citizens of a territory to determine free or slave status of future states
9. _____ A policy adopted in 1850 that urged southern states to compromise and not secede
10. _____ Supreme Court case that ruled slaves were not citizens and could not sue

```
Y R Z F A Y J T G T R N D V R F F N G U
V T S P F N E R Q V Q D A Q N L H M H Q
I P N P D I A D T T C Z V N R V B A V M
Q B Y G W T R N N L W D Q O G V N R R C
B R Y J I S K A T M D G N D K X D O S D
X E S K I E K T T E J I T V D I F I L P
P Z L G X D R M X L B X X Q K T V D A B
R C K H F T B E D T B E X S A Y R F V S
V F T D G S W D V D B J L L J E S B E R
T X R C T E K Z C O E V P L D V R O C E
R L P U L F F G X W S A Q S U L P X O D
K P X Y F I L L U N I R C P L M C X D E
M N X S W N H J F G Y O A L T S P E E C
T E V X N A K Z R F T O S L Y Z K S Q E
C B L U S M X O Q T B S A I U C M J S S
F Q L C F O E K K D L W Q U O P N U D N
U T C D P G W P H M J T F E G J O V D I
S E C T I O N A L I S M W P I N D P I O
O X N U T D S R Y Z E R B O Y Z M L Z A
B A R B A I L B K B S Y Q V G X H S M Z
```

Name_____   **Date**_____

Georgia's Decision to Secede

Directions: The decision for Georgia to secede was not automatic. Many politicians sensed that there could be tragic consequences for our state. Soon after Lincoln's election, Alexander Stephens argued that Georgia should not secede. Evaluate the excerpt from Stephens's speech and summarize its impact.

The first question that presents itself is, shall the people of Georgia secede from the Union in consequence of the election of Mr. Lincoln to the Presidency of the United States? My countrymen, I tell you frankly, candidly, and earnestly, that I do not think that they ought. In my judgment, the election of no man, constitutionally chosen to that high office, is sufficient cause to justify any State to separate from the Union. It ought to stand by and aid still in maintaining the Constitution of the country. To make a point of resistance to the Government, to withdraw from it because any man has been elected, would put us in the wrong. We are pledged to maintain the Constitution. Many of us have sworn to support it. Can we, therefore, for the mere election of any man to the Presidency, and that, too, in accordance with the prescribed forms of the Constitution, make a point of resistance to the Government, without becoming the breakers of that sacred instrument ourselves, by withdrawing ourselves from it? Would we not be in the wrong? Whatever fate is to befall this country, let it never be laid to the charge of the people of the South, and especially the people of Georgia, that we were untrue to our national engagements. Let the fault and the wrong rest upon others. If all our hopes are to be blasted, if the Republic is to go down, let us be found to the last moment standing on the deck with the Constitution of the United States waving over our heads. (Applause.) Let the fanatics of the North break the Constitution, if such is their fell purpose. Let the responsibility be upon them. I shall speak presently more of their acts; but let not the South, let us not be the ones to commit the aggression. We went into the election with this people. The result was different from what we wished; but the election has been constitutionally held. Were we to make a point of resistance to the Government and go out of the Union merely on that account, the record would be made up hereafter against us.

Source: A.D. Candler, comp., Confederate Records of the State of Georgia (1909), vol 1, pp. 183-205.

Your summary of Stephens's argument:

_____

_____

_____

_____

_____

_____

_____

NOTE: After secession, Alexander Stephens served as vice president of the Confederate States of America.

Name_____

Date_____

Taking Sides—North versus South

Directions: On the map below, color code the states that fought for the North or South. Also, mark the border states and territories.

Key:
Blue — North
Gray — South
Green — Border
Black — Territory

Name_____   Date_____

Civil War Diaries

Diaries and letters from ordinary citizens offer a unique glimpse into history. These people did not expect anyone to read their mail, so the perspectives they offer are often personal and unbiased.

Directions: Read the letter below and, on a separate sheet of paper, write a reply as if you were the father or mother responding to the letter.

Camp of the 36th Ohio Vet. Vol.
Infry., near Harpers Ferry
Aug. 7th. '64

Dear Father:

As I have a little time to spare, I will write you a few lines this morning. Should have written before but did not know where to direct so requested the letters I wrote home to be forwarded to you. No doubt you have heard before this all about our battle at Winchester and the different skirmishes we have been in. Have no time to give you a detailed account, as we expect to move every moment.

Our loss at Winchester now foots up 123 in killed & wounded, 11 killed, 112 wounded, 17 missing, Capt. Fort of Co. E., was killed, Lt. Montgomery, Haddow & Maj. Palmer wounded, 11 wounded & 2 missing. In my Co. none killed. Lt. George Putnam was wounded & fell into the hands of the enemy.

Our Regt. has lost some 200 men since we came into Va. When our old men go out will have but a small squad left. I have made up my mind to leave the service if I can be mustered out. If not I will resign this fall. I am feeling pretty well, with the exception of being very tired and wore out from hard marching and loss of sleep. Have marched almost every day since we left Parkersburg, fighting a good part of the time. I believe I have suffered more than I did on our Lynchburg raid. This is the fourth time we have passed through Harpers Ferry.

Have not heard a word from home since I left. Would like to hear from Luther. It is reported that Gen. Grant came in on the train last evening. Gen. Crook is Brevet Maj. Gen. & commands the forces in the field. The 4th and part of the 19th Corps are here in Kanawha troops. The rebels are reported in a dozen different places some at Hagerstown, some at Cumberland, some crossing at Hancock, some reported in trenching on old Antietam battleground. I think but few (rebel) infantry have crossed into Pa. only Cavalry. They are raiding through the country while Gen. Early's forces gather the crops in Shenandoah Valley.

Orderly is calling for the letters. Direct 1st Brig 2nd Infry Div Crooks Comd.
Your aff son
J. G. Barker
Excuse poor writing am sitting on ground under shelter tent.

Name_____   **Date**_____

Anaconda Plan

The Anaconda Plan is the name widely given to a strategy for subduing the Confederate states that emphasized the blockade of southern ports and an advance down the Mississippi River to cut the South in two. The name "Anaconda" refers to the suffocating effect this would have on the South—like the coils of an anaconda snake would have on its victim.

Directions: Examine the political cartoon on the right and then answer the questions to evaluate its meaning.

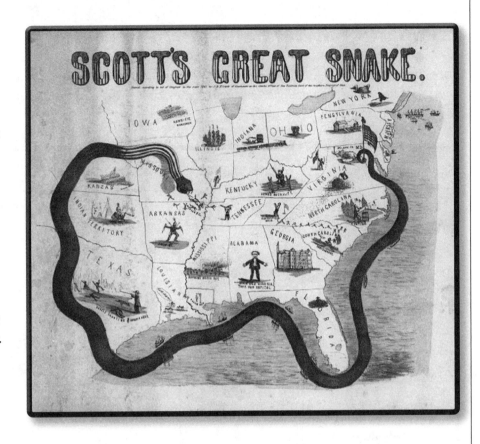

1. Describe the North's strategy. _____
   _____

2. List objects or people you see in the cartoon. (Place an asterisk next to the two or three you think are most important.) _____
   _____

3. What are the most important words on the cartoon? _____
   _____

4. Explain the message of the cartoon. _____
   _____

5. What do you think the artist/author wanted the reader to learn from this cartoon? _____
   _____

6. When and where do you think this cartoon was published and why? _____
   _____

Name_____   **Date**_____

Compare Civil War Battles

Directions: It's hard to imagine that years ago warfare may have been waged near your home. Go to Internet site **www.americancivilwar.com**. Under Featured Indexes, click on State Battle Maps, then click on Georgia, Pennsylvania, and Maryland. Fill in the chart below.

	Chickamauga	Gettysburg	Atlanta	Antietam
When				
What State				
Estimated Union Casualties				
Estimated Confederate Casualties				
Results				
Principal Commanders				

© Clairmont Press, Inc. DO NOT DUPLICATE 1-800-874-8638

Name_____   Date_____

Timeline of Key Civil War Events

Directions: Identify the month and year that each of the events below took place. Then, use that list to make a timeline of key events in the Civil War period.

Month/Year

_____ Lincoln's first election   _____ Battle of Chickamauga

_____ South Carolina secedes   _____ Battle of Antietam

_____ Fort Sumter   _____ Sherman captures Atlanta

_____ Georgia secedes   _____ Sherman captures Savannah

_____ Battle of Gettysburg   _____ War ends with Lee's surrender

_____ Emancipation Proclamation goes into effect

| 1860 | 1861 | 1862 | 1863 | 1864 | 1865 |

Name_____

Date_____

Civil War People, Terms, and Events

Directions: Use the chart below to reinforce your Civil War vocabulary.

Vocabulary Word	Sentence Containing the Word	Picture That Represents the Word
Blockade		
Emancipation Proclamation		
Antietam		
Chickamauga		
Andersonville Prison		
March to the Sea		
Secession		
Robert E. Lee		
William T. Sherman		
Jefferson Davis		

Name_____   Date_____

Presidential Reconstruction Plan

Directions: Read or review pages 419-422 and answer the questions below. If the information is not in your textbook, look it up!

1. Under Lincoln's plan for Reconstruction, how many voters had to take the oath of loyalty before a new state government could be formed? Why do you think this number was so low? _____
   _____
   _____

2. What was Andrew Johnson's goal for Reconstruction? _____
   _____
   _____
   _____

3. When was the 13th Amendment to the U.S. Constitution ratified, and what did it declare? _____
   _____
   _____

4. Who did Georgians choose as their two senators during Reconstruction? _____
   _____

5. Why did the election of these two men upset northerners? _____
   _____
   _____

6. In March 1865, Abraham Lincoln said that he wanted to "bind up the nation's wounds." How did Lincoln's plan for Reconstruction reflect Lincoln's desires? _____
   _____
   _____
   _____

7. What might have happened if the South had refused to adhere to Reconstruction guidelines? _____
   _____
   _____
   _____

Name_____   **Date**_____

Constitutional Amendments During Reconstruction

In relatively short order after the Civil War, the United States approved three constitutional amendments aimed at ending slavery once and for all while also ensuring the civil rights of the newly freed slaves.

Directions: Review the textbook and other sources for information on these amendments, and complete the chart below.

Amendment	When Ratifiied	Purpose	Impact on Georgians
Thirteenth			
Fourteenth			
Fifteenth			

Discussion Question: What role do you believe the actions of Georgia and other southern states played in the passage of these amendments? Would these have been necessary had the southern states complied with the intent of Reconstruction?

Name_____   Date_____

Review of Economic and Social Reconstruction

Directions: Review pages 430-439, close your textbooks, and then answer the following questions **T** for True or **F** for False. With a partner or in a small group, compare and discuss your answers. Then, open your textbooks and search for quotes that support your answers. If your original answer is wrong, simply change it and write the quote.

T   F   1. The Freedmen's Bureau was founded to assist only recently freed slaves.

(Quote: including page #) _____

_____

T   F   2. After the war, President Johnson promised a mule and 40 acres of land to all recently freed slaves.

(Quote: including page #) _____

_____

T   F   3. The Freedmen's Bureau helped establish a standard freedman wage at $12 per day.

(Quote: including page #) _____

_____

T   F   4. Former slaves and poor whites who had their own mules and tools but no land often became tenant farmers.

(Quote: including page #) _____

_____

T   F   5. The convict lease system was intended to ensure that prisoners were treated fairly.

(Quote: including page #)_____

_____

T   F   6.   After the war, many churches divided based on the race of church members.

(Quote: including page #)_____

_____

T   F   7. During Reconstruction, Georgia passed the first state laws for public education.

(Quote: including page #) _____

_____

Name_____ **Date**_____

Reconstruction Categories

Directions: Although the changes brought about during Reconstruction were wide ranging, they can generally be grouped into one of three areas: Economic, Political, and Social. In teams or small groups, each student should list ideas that fit under each topic. Students should then share ideas in groups and add to existing lists. Completed lists will have several ideas under each heading.

Economic:

Political:

Social:

Additional Ideas: Students can make a poster over all topics or write a short paper on the topics.

Name_____ **Date**_____

The People Who Impacted Reconstruction

Directions: Identify the significant contribution of each individual listed below as it pertains to the era of Reconstruction.

1. President Abraham Lincoln _____

_____

2. President Andrew Johnson _____

_____

3. Governor Charles Jones Jenkins _____

_____

4. Alexander Stephens and Hershel Johnson _____

_____

5. General George Meade _____

_____

6. Henry McNeal Turner _____

_____

7. General Nathan Bedford Forrest _____

_____

8. General Alfred H. Terry _____

_____

9. Robert Toombs and Charles Jones Jenkins _____

_____

Name_____ Date_____

The Bourbon Triumvirate

The period immediately following Reconstruction saw a tug-of-war for political control in Georgia. In general, Republicans sought to change the "old ways" while Democratic politicians sought to maintain the pre-Civil War status quo.

Directions: Read Section 1 and fill in the following information concerning the Bourbon Triumvirate era.

1. Define *triumvirate.* _____

   _____

2. List the men who made up the triumvirate and indicate the political positions that they held.

   a. _____

   b. _____

   c. _____

3. Although Democrats held the upper hand in Georgia politics, the Republican Party was alive and well. Explain the difference between "black and tan" and "lily white" Republicans. _____

   _____

   _____

   _____

4. How did the Bourbon Democrats feel about state money? _____

   _____

   _____

   _____

5. What were some of the ideas that the Democratic Party emphasized that allowed them to appeal to most white voters? _____

   _____

   _____

   _____

6. **Discussion Question:** The textbook indicates that the Independents held some influence in Georgia politics during this time. Compare this situation to modern Georgia where there is little evidence of a third political party at all. What are the advantages and disadvantages of political parties? Is it better for a democratic society to have more or fewer political parties? Why?

Name_____ Date_____

Tom Watson and the Populists

Directions: Read Section 2 and review some of the reasons poor farmers were angry. Answer the following questions using the word bank below.

Word Bank

Populist Party	Tom Watson
racism	electricity
graduated income tax	secret ballot
white power	vice president
Farmers' Alliance	fraud
telephones	Grange

1. Poor farmers across America united for increased political influence. Two of the first organizations they formed were the _____ and the _____.

2. As the influence of the Farmers' Alliance declined, a new political organization called the

   _____ emerged with many of the same beliefs.

3. One effect of populism was the stirring of racial tensions. Democrats tried to keep white voters by appealing to _____ and preserving _____.

4. _____ and _____ were two modern conveniences that many farmers did not have access to.

5. The Farmers' Alliance wanted several political reforms. Two examples of these reforms were

   _____ and _____.

6. _____ was a leading figure in the Populist Party.

7. Tom Watson was nominated to run for _____ in the Populist Party.

8. _____ is the practice of dishonest voting or counting of votes.

Name_____   **Date**_____

Evaluate a Political Cartoon

Directions: Using your textbook and the political cartoon on page 458, answer the questions below to evaluate the meaning of the cartoon.

Level 1	
Visuals	**Words**
1. List the objects or people you see in the cartoon.	1. Identify the cartoon caption and title. 2. Locate two words or phrases used by the cartoonist to identify objects or people within the cartoon. 3. Record any important dates or numbers that appear in the cartoon.
Level 2	
Visuals	**Words**
1. Which objects on your list are symbols? 2. What do you think each symbol means?	1. Which words or phrases appear to be most significant? Why do you think so? 2. List adjectives that describe the emotions portrayed in the cartoon.
Level 3	
A. Describe the action taking place in the cartoon.	A.
B. Explain how the words in the cartoon clarify symbols.	B.
C. Explain the message of the cartoon.	C.
D. What special interest groups would agree/disagree with the cartoon's message? Why?	D.

Name_____   **Date**_____

Progressive Project

Directions: Review the textbook and look for the ideas that the progressives supported. Then, imagine you are an advertising artist hired by Hoke Smith to make a poster for a campaign event in his governorship race. Sketch your ideas for a poster here to convince a citizen to attend the meeting and vote for Hoke Smith.

Name_____   **Date**_____

Plessy v. Ferguson

Directions: Review the information concerning the *Plessy v. Ferguson* case. Imagine you are a reporter who just heard the Supreme Court decision in the case. Write an article for your hometown paper that summarizes the key points of the case and the establishment of the separate-but-equal doctrine as supported by the Supreme Court.

_____

_____

_____

_____

_____

_____

_____

_____

_____

_____

_____

_____

_____

_____

_____

_____

_____

_____

_____

Name_____   **Date**_____

Key African Americans of This Era

Directions: Review the textbook to compare notes on these influential individuals.

	Influential Individual	**Known For**
Homer Plessy		
Henry McNeal Turner		
Booker T. Washington		
W. E. B. DuBois		
John and Lugenia Burns Hope		

Name_____   Date_____

Vocabulary Crossword Puzzle

Directions: Use the clues below to complete the crossword puzzle for a vocabulary review.

Across

2. separation of blacks and whites
9. leader of African American community, born into slavery, first leader of Tuskegee Institute
10. laws and ordinances that enable segregation

Down

1. take away the right to vote
3. white supremacy group
4. African American leader who proposed sending the "Talented Tenth" to college for a liberal arts education
5. massive movement of African Americans from south to north
6. murder by a mob, usually by hanging or shooting
7. challenged Louisiana law that segregated blacks and whites on railroad cars
8. organization designed to enhance opportunities for African Americans

Name_____   **Date**_____

Importance of Cotton

Directions: As a class, or as individuals, use your favorite search engine to collect information about Georgia's cotton production over time. Compile your own notes and prepare to share them in small or large groups.

Questions to Explore:

1. Look for the number of bales of cotton produced in Georgia over time, including modern history.

2. Find out more information about the impact of the boll weevil.

3. How much cotton does Georgia produce today?

4. What region of the state grows cotton today?

5. Find out about the growth of textile mills after Reconstruction.

6. Brainstorm with classmates other questions of particular interest.

Suggested Websites:

♦ The New Georgia Encyclopedia

♦ Georgia Department of Agriculture

♦ _____

♦ _____

♦ _____

Suggested Strategy:

The teacher can provide students with three to five post-it notes to collect their individual facts. Students can assemble these notes to tell the "story" of cotton in Georgia.

Name_____ Date_____

World War I Posters

Directions: Use a Primary Document Evaluation Sheet to examine these posters in detail. Are they true, or are they propaganda? Can propaganda also be true?

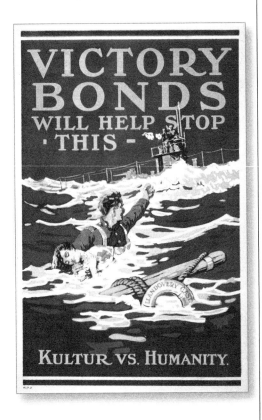

Differentiation Idea: Teachers can use Internet searches to offer a larger variety of posters for evaluation or might assign a project for students to develop their own posters with Georgia-specific themes such as growing food for the troops.

Name_____   **Date**_____

Impact of World War I on Georgia

Directions: Review Section 2 and fill in the information below. Think about how the war impacted Georgians.

1. When World War I first started, the United States chose to remain neutral. Describe *neutrality*.

    _____

    _____

    _____

    _____

2. How did the sinking of the *Lusitania* contribute to the United States' entry into the war?

    _____

    _____

    _____

    _____

Issue	Impact In/On Georgia
Draft	
Military Bases	
Economy	

Name_____   **Date**_____

Key Terms

Directions: Use each of the following terms from Chapter 20 in a sentence. Review the definitions in the chapter to assist you.

1. New South: _____

    _____

2. diversity: _____

    _____

3. truck farming: _____

    _____

4. textile industry: _____

    _____

5. boll weevil: _____

    _____

6. isolationism: _____

    _____

7. the *Lusitania:* _____

    _____

8. armistice: _____

    _____

9. pandemic: _____

    _____

10. World War I: _____

    _____

Name_____   Date_____

Electricity is Here!

Directions: Imagine you live in Georgia in the 1920s. Your home has just had electricity installed for the first time. Think about the main ways that a few simple electric household or farm tools might change your life. Write a letter to a friend or relative describing how electricity has changed your life or daily routine.

_____

_____

_____

_____

_____

_____

_____

_____

_____

_____

_____

_____

_____

_____

_____

Name_____   Date_____

Transporting Georgia's Products Over Time

Directions: So far this year, we have examined a few thousand years of Georgia history. Beginning with the Paleo peoples, let's pause now to think about the products grown or manufactured in Georgia over time, and how these items were transported to markets. Develop a chart to show the evolution of Georgia's economy and transport systems/technologies. This could be a group or individual project.

Era	Transport Technology Available in This Era	Goods Grown or Produced in This Era
Before European contact		
Colonial		
Civil War/Reconstruction		
1920s and beyond		

Name_____   Date_____

The Ku Klux Klan

Directions: The Ku Klux Klan (KKK) was notorious for its treatment of African Americans and certain other groups. Read page 532 and answer the following questions.

1. What were some of the postwar fears that helped spur the growth of the KKK? _____
_____
_____

2. Besides blacks, what other groups did the KKK target? _____
_____

3. What were some specific ways the KKK executed its terror campaign? _____
_____
_____

4. What do you think motivated individuals to join the KKK? _____
_____
_____

5. What did Julian Harris do in response to the KKK activities? _____
_____
_____

6. What do you think motivated Mr. Harris? _____
_____
_____

7. How do you feel about hate groups such as the KKK today? _____
_____
_____

8. What are some ways we can avoid hate within our schools and communities today? _____
_____
_____
_____

Name_____   Date_____

The 1920s Bring Change

Directions: Using the textbook, categorize the many changes that occurred in Georgia during the 1920s. (Some items may fit into multiple categories.)

Social Issues: List issues that impacted personal interactions.

_____
_____
_____
_____
_____
_____
_____
_____

Economic Issues: List ways that the economy grew or changed.

_____
_____
_____
_____
_____
_____
_____
_____

Technologies: List technological developments that impacted lives.

_____
_____
_____
_____
_____
_____
_____
_____

Differentiation Ideas: Have students develop their own categories. Ask students to prioritize changes and defend their reasons.

Name_____ **Date**_____

Georgia Moves Into the Great Depression

Directions: Read the statements below and circle **T** for True or **F** for False. Next, review Section 2 to find out if your answers were correct. Find a brief quote from the textbook that supports each answer. If you answered incorrectly, just change your answer and write the quote.

T F   1. Just after World War I, cotton prices increased and farmers in Georgia did quite well.

_____

T F   2. Around 1915, Georgia's farmers battled an insect called the cotton weevil before it did great damage to crops.

_____

T F   3. Georgia suffered from drought conditions from 1925 to 1927.

_____

T F   4. Prior to the depression, industrial factories were the first place where whites and blacks worked together.

_____

T F   5. Industries grew during the 1920s and eventually employed almost 50 percent of Georgia's workforce.

_____

T F   6. The Great Depression was caused by the stock market crash of 1929.

_____

T F   7. Overproduction occurs when an industry produces more goods than it can sell.

_____

T F   8. Tariffs established by the United States helped solve the Great Depression.

_____

T F   9. When banks closed during the Great Depression, depositors simply lost their money.

_____

Name_____   **Date**_____

Vocabulary Crossword Puzzle

Directions: Use the clues below to complete the crossword puzzle.

Across

2. first man to fly solo across the Atlantic Ocean
4. a modern convenience that made work at home and on the farm easier
7. means of moving most freight through Georgia
8. means of transportation that became affordable through mass production
9. a more common sight in the sky after World War I

Down

1. the construction of homes and movement of people away from cities
3. young women of the 1920s
5. installation of these in homes greatly improved communications
6. source of news and entertainment for families gathered around it

Name_____   **Date**_____

Franklin Delano Roosevelt and Georgia

Directions: Two years into the Great Depression, FDR was elected president. He referred to Georgia as "my other state." Review Section 1 and fill in the chart.

What state was he from?	Where in Georgia did Roosevelt visit to improve his condition?

What high office did he hold in his native state before becoming president?	What was the name given to the group of policies that Roosevelt used to help the U.S. during the Great Depression?

What disease left him paralyzed?	How many Georgia delegates voted for FDR at the Democratic National Convention?

Why do you think Roosevelt called Georgia "my other state"?

Name_____   **Date**_____

Letter to the White House

Directions: During the Great Depression, many children wrote letters directly to President Franklin Roosevelt and First Lady Eleanor Roosevelt to appeal for help. Imagine you are a young child living in poverty here in Georgia. What would you need help with? Are you hungry? Do your parents need a job? Write a letter to President Roosevelt or Mrs. Roosevelt explaining your situation and asking for the help you think your family needs the most.

_____

_____

_____

_____

_____

_____

_____

_____

_____

_____

_____

_____

_____

_____

_____

Differentiation Idea: Have students use search engines to locate letters to FDR during the Great Depression. They can share the letters with the class and/or use these letters as models or ideas for writing their own letters.

Name_____   **Date**_____

Evaluate a Primary Document

Directions: Historians value primary documents such as letters, diaries, and photographs because they offer an unfiltered view of events. As we have seen, Georgia's agricultural economy was suffering even before the depression began. Use this photograph to evaluate the condition of this Georgia farmer. Use the available visual clues to imagine what his life was like.

The cotton sharecropper's unit is one mule and the land he can cultivate with a one-horse plow. Greene County, Georgia, Dorothea Lange, photographer, 1937.

Some questions to consider:

1. What do you think a typical day was like for a farmer like this? _____
    _____

2. How was technology impacting a farmer like this? _____
    _____

3. How common was this sight in Georgia? _____
    _____

4. What would the future hold for this family? _____
    _____

5. What was the man in this photo thinking? _____
    _____

Name_____   Date_____

The Civilian Conservation Corps

Directions: Use the textbook to answer the first three questions, and then search online to answer the remaining questions.

1.   How much money did a CCC worker earn and how much did he have to send home? _____
_____

2.   List at least three projects completed by the CCC in Georgia. _____
_____

3.   How many total camps and men participated in Georgia? _____
_____

Use the Internet for the following questions. (A list of search sites is shown below.)

4.   How many states had CCC camps/projects? _____
_____

5.   How many young men participated in the program? _____
_____

6.   List the most interesting project/place you can find. _____
_____
_____

Suggested search sites to begin:

Georgiaencyclopedia.org

National Park Service

National Forest Service

Grand Canyon National Park

Yosemite National Park

Differentiation Idea: Pick one CCC project you read about, and write a letter home as if you were in the camp working on the project.

Name_____ Date_____

The Alphabet Soup of the New Deal

Directions: Before he took office, Roosevelt promised swift action to tackle the problems of the Great Depression. Many programs were known by their initials, and there were so many programs some people called them alphabet soup. Write the name of the program below the acronym and, in the block provided, explain what the program accomplished.

Program	Purpose of Program and How It Helped Georgians
FDIC	
CCC	
NRA	
PWA	
FERA	
SSA	
NYA	
REA	

Name_____   Date_____

Key Events Leading to U.S. Entry into World War II

Directions: Review Section 1 and summarize the key events leading to the U.S. entry into the war.

Event	How This Contributed to the War
Emergence of military dictators in Japan, Germany, and Italy	
The treatment of Germany in the Treaty of Versailles	
Japanese expansion in Asia	
U.S. economic dependence on global trade	
The 1939 German invasion of Poland and then other countries	
The Japanese attack on Pearl Harbor, December 7, 1941	

Name_____   **Date**_____

Debating U.S. Involvement in World War II

Directions: Prior to the attack on Pearl Harbor, Americans struggled with what to do about the war raging in Europe and Japan's expansion in the Far East. There were strong arguments both for and against U.S. involvement in the war. Read Section 1 to gain some context for the American position on the war. Depending on instructions from your teacher, take notes in either the pro or con column below as you read. Prepare to debate these issues with your classmates.

(PRO) We Should Enter the War Now	(CON) We Should Avoid This War

Some points to consider: (1) Economics of the Great Depression, (2) The human cost of World War II, (3) Is the war really affecting us?, (4) What if Hitler wins?

Name_____   **Date**_____

World War II Impacts Georgia

Directions: Review Section 2 and write important facts that would fit each category. Put at least three to five facts in each section.

1. How World War II helped bring Georgia out of the Great Depression:

   _____
   _____
   _____
   _____
   _____

2. Growth of military bases in Georgia:

   _____
   _____
   _____
   _____
   _____

3. The growth of defense industries in Georgia:

   _____
   _____
   _____
   _____
   _____

4. Life in Georgia during the war:

   _____
   _____
   _____
   _____
   _____

Name_____

Date_____

The Holocaust

Directions: Review the section on the Holocaust and answer the following questions.

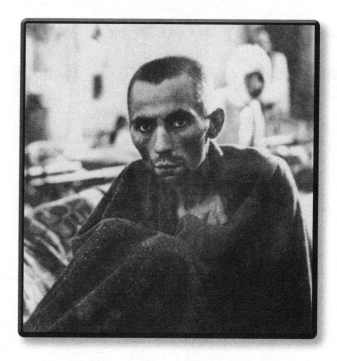

1. Define *Holocaust.* _____
    _____

2. Besides Jews, what other groups or individuals were targeted in the Holocaust? _____
    _____
    _____

3. What was the "final solution"? _____
    _____
    _____

4. Define *genocide.* _____
    _____

5. According to the textbook, what is the role of Atlanta in Jewish culture? _____
    _____
    _____

Discussion Questions:

6. Discuss/evaluate the picture above.
7. What parallels exist between the Holocaust and the white supremacy movement?
8. What steps can you take to ensure an event like the Holocaust is never repeated?

Name_____ Date_____

Vocabulary Scramble

Directions: Unscramble the words below and fill in the blanks for a vocabulary review.

1. In Germany and Italy, militaristic _____ (tatrocdis) emerged and began to threaten European countries.

2. The treaty of _____ (asilrlesve), which ended World War I, placed harsh economic penalties on Germany.

3. Japan began to take over areas in Southeast Asia in order to secure much needed _____ _____ (war atrelasmi) such as oil and coal.

4. _____ (sifmacs) is a form of government led by a dictator who believes in the superiority of a particular group.

5. The German army preferred a tactic known as _____ (zkreitlbig), which means lightning war.

6. The United States initially adopted a position of _____ (tyreanulti) with regard to the war in Europe.

7. Under _____ - _____ (denl-seeal), certain war-related materials were provided to friendly European countries at no immediate cost.

8. While _____ (relhti) led Germany into war, _____ (susonliim) led Italy to form an alliance with Germany.

9. The Japanese surprise attack on _____ (learp rabroh) in December 1941 finally drew the U.S. into the world war.

10. During the _____ (costhloau), over 6 million Jews were killed by Hitler's regime.

11. The deliberate murder of an entire group of people is known as _____ (doienecg).

Name_____   **Date**_____

Georgia State Flags

Directions: Sketch pictures of the former and current state flags. Then, evaluate the significance of the symbolism associated with these flags.

Pre-1956 Flag

1956 Flag

2001-2003 Flag

Current Flag

Discussion Questions:

1. What do flags tell us about the people and cultures they represent? What kinds of symbolism are commonly used on state and national flags?
2. Identify the significant political/social issues at stake during the era of each flag.
3. What do symbols, such as flags, say about a state or a nation?
4. If you were to design a flag for our state today, what symbols/colors would you choose?

Name_____   Date_____

Civil Rights Protests Challenge the U.S. Legal System and Provoke Change

Although the civil rights movement involved thousands of people and hundreds of challenges to the social structure of the South, we can grasp the intensity of the overall effort by understanding a few of its more well-known events.

Directions: Match the events in the right column with the descriptions provided on the left.

_____ 1. President Eisenhower used federal troops to force this action.

_____ 2. The U.S. Court of Appeals determined that the white primary was unconstitutional.

_____ 3. This U.S. Supreme Court decision overturned *Plessy v. Ferguson.*

_____ 4. This group recommended that school desegregation in Georgia be left to local districts.

_____ 5. This was a move by the legislature, approved by the voters, in 1953.

_____ 6. Georgia citizens had no vote in this legislative response to the *Brown v. Board of Education* ruling.

_____ 7. A U.S. court order led to this action in school integration.

_____ 8. This U.S. Supreme Court decision declared "separate-but-equal" to be constitutionally acceptable.

A. 1956 flag controversy

B. *Brown v. Board of Education*

C. Sibley Commission

D. integration of the University of Georgia

E. integration of Little Rock Central High School

F. *Plessy v. Ferguson*

G. Georgia constitutional amendment to prevent school integration

H. *King v. Chapman*

Discussion Questions: Talk about how all three branches of government—executive, judicial and legislative—worked for and against the civil rights movement.

Name_____   Date_____

The Role of Presidents, Governors, and Atlanta Mayors in the Civil Rights Movement

Directions: Review the chapter and summarize the roles that these important political leaders played in the civil rights movement.

Political Leader	Significant Event(s) and Their Contribution(s)
President Harry Truman	
President Dwight Eisenhower	
President John Kennedy	
President Lyndon Johnson	
Governor Herman Talmadge	
Governor Ernest Vandiver	
Mayor William Hartsfield	
Mayor Ivan Allen, Jr.	
Mayor Maynard Jackson	

Name_____   **Date**_____

Get Involved in the Civil Rights Movement

As the civil rights movement gained momentum, thousands of African Americans and whites took bold steps to challenge the status quo. Often, through their actions, they put themselves at risk for physical harm. Many of the protesters were not much older than you. What motivated these courageous people to take such steps?

Directions: In Section 2, review the founding of the Student Nonviolent Coordinating Committee. Imagine your classroom is a small office and you are preparing for a night of guest speakers to address the civil rights movement. Design a poster/flyer to advertise the meeting. Sketch your idea in the space below.

Name_____   Date_____

Civil Rights Icons

Directions: Many civil rights leaders were from the South and Georgia in particular. Use the textbook and the Internet to describe the roles and key events these individuals participated in.

Civil Rights Icon	Role/Key Events Participated In
Rabbi Jacob Rothschild	
Hamilton Holmes	
Charlayne Hunter	
Rosa Parks	
Dr. Martin Luther King, Jr.	
John Lewis	
Dr. Benjamin Mays	
Andrew Young	

Name_____   **Date**_____

Understanding the County Unit System

Directions: Use the space below to draw a political cartoon that addresses the county unit system. The cartoon can be either for or against the system, and it must include information about differing "votes" depending on the size of the county. Then, write a few sentences evaluating your own cartoon, just as you have done for other artists' cartoons previously.

_____

_____

_____

_____

_____

_____

_____

Name_____ **Date**_____

Key Politicians in Post-World War II Georgia

After World War II, Georgians entered an era of political changes. Some political leaders tried to hold onto the old social norms while others began to challenge and change the old social structure.

Directions: Choose one of the political leaders listed below (or use a leader assigned by the teacher) and review his position on key issues facing Georgians. Based on this knowledge, design a poster that "advertises" your politician and his positions.

Carl Vinson, Richard Russell, Ellis Arnall, Herman Talmadge, Eugene Talmadge

Name_____   Date_____

The U.S. Constitution Shapes Georgia Politics

After the Civil War, several amendments to the U.S. Constitution helped change the political and power structure in Georgia.

Directions: Review your textbook and the constitutional amendments listed below. Add notes to the blanks provided in order to understand how these amendments changed Georgia.

U.S. Constitutional Amendment	What the Amendment Did	Impact of the Amendment on Georgia Politics
Thirteenth		
Fourteenth		
Fifteenth		
Seventeenth		
Nineteenth		

Name_____   **Date**_____

The Political Career of Jimmy Carter

Directions: Review Section 2 and summarize the political career of Jimmy Carter by answering the questions below.

1. Which Georgia city is Jimmy Carter's hometown? _____

2. Where did he go to college, and what was his first career? _____

   _____

3. What family business did he run in the 1950s? _____

   _____

4. How many terms did he serve as state senator? _____

5. What were two specific areas of concern while Carter was senator? _____

   _____

6. In what year was he elected governor? _____

7. List some of the key actions that Carter took as governor. _____

   _____

   _____

   _____

8. In what year was Carter elected president? _____

9. What were the Camp David Accords? _____

   _____

   _____

10. What were the results of the presidential election of 1980? Based on your reading, why do you think the election turned out that way? _____

   _____

   _____

Name_____   **Date**_____

Moving Goods Across Georgia

Directions: Pick a location in Georgia at least 100 miles from Savannah and presume you are a merchant who needs to move one ton of goods to the port. Use your best judgment to estimate the miles per hour for your calculations. Think about the problems the various means of transport might encounter. What if your goods are perishable, such as fruit? Can your mode of transport move 24 hours a day? Does your driver/operator need rest? Fill in the chart below with your answers.

Means of Transport	Estimated Miles per Hour	How Long It Will Take and Other Considerations
Colonial: Horse/Wagon on a turnpike		
Civil War: Railroads		
Post-World War II: Interstate Highway		

Name_____ **Date**_____

Impact of Farming Technology

Directions: Evaluate the pictures below and consider the wide-ranging impacts of farm mechanization.

1. How does the invention and use of mechanized farm equipment impact individual farmers? _____

   _____

2. As mechanization was introduced to farmers, what (do you think) happened to family farms?_____

   _____

   _____

3. What are some advantages of mechanization? _____

   _____

4. What are some possible disadvantages of mechanization? _____

   _____

5. Think about the daily lives of the farmers in these pictures. How are they similar/different?_____

   _____

   _____

Name_____   **Date**_____

Industry Changes in Georgia

For many years, agriculture dominated the economy in Georgia. Although some industries grew after Reconstruction, the real industry growth occurred during and after World War II.

Directions: Review Section 3 and consider the impacts of changing industries in Georgia.

1. Mining and Forestry:

   a. Which geographic region is known for marble and granite? _____

   b. What white clay mineral is abundant along the Fall Line? _____

   c. How did rail lines contribute to a successful kaolin industry? _____
   _____

   d. What are some items that rely on kaolin for production? _____
   _____

   e. What nationally known paper company is headquartered in Atlanta, Georgia?_____
   _____

2. Fiber Industries:

   a. What were some textile products provided by Georgia in World War II? _____
   _____

   b. How did improved equipment technology affect textile workers? _____
   _____

   c. How did international competition impact Georgians? _____
   _____

3. Military and Defense:

   a. How do military installations contribute to Georgia's economy? _____
   _____

   b. What aircraft company currently builds planes in Marietta? _____
   _____

Name_____ **Date**_____

Plan a Trip to Hartsfield-Jackson Atlanta International Airport

Directions: Follow these instructions and answer the questions to plan a trip for you and your family.

1. Pick a place that you would like to fly to and visit: _____

2. Use your favorite Internet search engine to locate an airline to find flight information:

    a. What day will you depart? _____

    b. What day will you return? _____

    c. What time does your flight leave the airport? _____

    d. How much will tickets cost for your family? _____

3. Plan your trip to the airport:

    a. What route will you drive from your house to the airport? _____

    _____

    _____

    b. How many miles will you drive? _____

    c. What time do you need to leave your house to catch your flight? (Don't forget the time needed to get through

    security.) _____

4. Questions to consider:

    a. If Hartsfield-Jackson was not in Georgia, where would you probably fly from? _____

    _____

    b. Could you catch a commuter flight to Atlanta from a nearby city? _____

    _____

Name_____

Date_____

Personal Saving and Investing Terms

Directions: Complete the crossword puzzle to review vocabulary for saving and investing.

Across

2. federal agency that ensures deposits at banks
9. an investment in something physical like property
10. an investment where the investor buys a portion of the company

Down

1. an investment in a financial instrument

3. an investment that pays a specific amount of interest once a specific amount of time has passed
4. buying more than a person can afford
5. money that an individual acquires
6. spending money for various purposes
7. pools money from various investors to buy stocks or bonds
8. a loan or advance used to buy something with a promise to pay in the future

Name_____ **Date**_____

Education Improvement Events

Directions: Review Section 1 of this chapter for information on the evolution of the education system in Georgia. Create a timeline of key people and events leading to our educational system today. You may want to include events you read about in previous chapters, such as the *Brown v. Board of Education* decision.

Name_____   **Date**_____

Make a T-Shirt

Directions: Artists show their creativity in many media. Now that we are at the end of the textbook, you know a lot about Georgia and its history. Pick a topic of your choosing and design a T-shirt that reflects your creativity. Have a classroom contest to see whose design is best, funniest, etc.

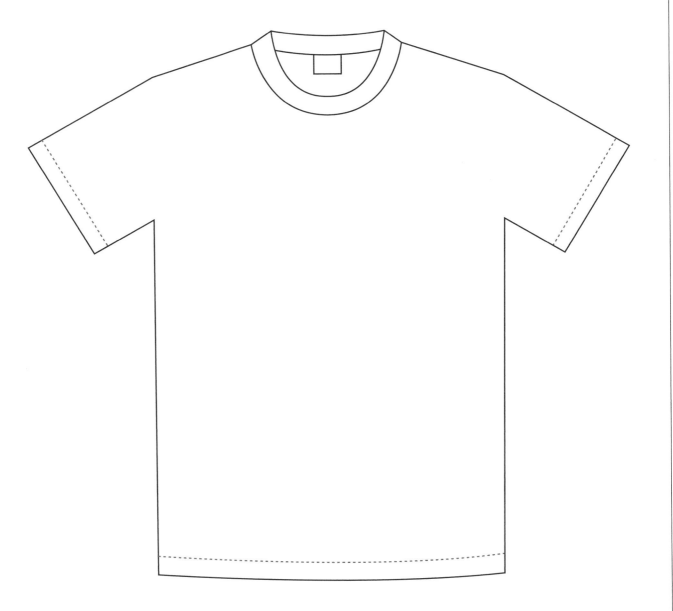

Name_____ **Date**_____

Assemble a Virtual Art Gallery

Directions: Using the artists mentioned in the book as well as others you may know of, use your favorite search engine and appropriate software to assemble pictures of their artwork or pictures that represent the artists. Remember, art comes in many forms including painting, music, etc. Use the space below to make a bibliography of where you found the pictures for your gallery.

1. Music:

   a. "Fiddlin'" John Carson _____

   b. Brenda Lee _____

   c. Ray Charles _____

   d. Alan Jackson _____

   e. Travis Tritt _____

   f. Trisha Yearwood _____

   g. Blind Willie McTell _____

   h. Gertrude "Ma" Rainey _____

   i. Little Richard _____

   j. James Brown _____

   k. Allman Brothers _____

   l. B-52s _____

   m. R.E.M. _____

   n. Widespread Panic _____

   o. Ludacris _____

   p. OutKast _____

   q. Robert Shaw _____

   r. Jessye Norman _____

2. Visual Artists:

   a. Benny Andrews _____

   b. Lamar Dodd _____

3. Others: _____

Name_____   **Date**_____

Design a New State Flag

Directions: Artists display their thoughts and ideas through their art. The last section of the chapter discusses the history and heritage of Georgia. You have studied many years of Georgia history and many remarkable people and events. Take some time to consider the state you call home and come up with a design for a new state flag that represents themes and ideas you think reflect Georgia today. Sketch your idea in the space provided below. Then, write a few sentences explaining why you chose your design and what you hope it will come to represent for Georgia citizens.

_____

_____

_____

_____

_____

_____